W9-AXS-411

**Illustrative Mathematics**®
LEARN MATH FOR LIFE

# GRADE 6

## Units

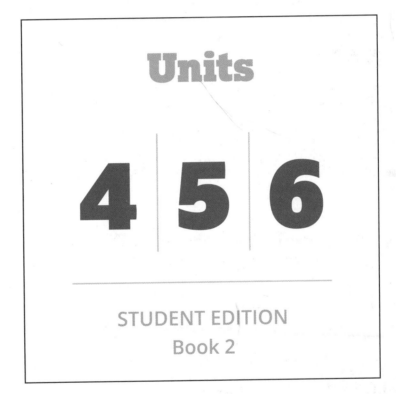

## 4 5 6

STUDENT EDITION
Book 2

**Kendall Hunt** | **iM** CERTIFIED®

*Warming Up to Decimals*

*Adding and Subtracting Decimals*

*Multiplying Decimals*

*Dividing Decimals*

*Let's Put It to Work*

*Equations in One Variable*

*Equal and Equivalent*

*Expressions with Exponents*

*Relationships Between Quantities*

*Let's Put it to Work*

**Illustrative Mathematics®**

LEARN MATH FOR LIFE

# GRADE 6

**Unit**

# 4

STUDENT EDITION

Book 2

**Kendall Hunt** |

# Lesson 1: Size of Divisor and Size of Quotient

Let's explore quotients of different sizes.

## 1.1: Number Talk: Size of Dividend and Divisor

Find the value of each expression mentally.

$5,000 \div 5$    1,000

$5,000 \div 2,500$    2

$5,000 \div 10,000$    .5

$5,000 \div 500,000$    .01

## 1.2: All Stacked Up

1. Here are several types of objects. For each type of object, estimate how many are in a stack that is 5 feet high. Be prepared to explain your reasoning.

Cardboard boxes

Notebooks

 5

 100

Bricks

Coins

 30

 5,000

iM KH

2. A stack of books is 72 inches tall. Each book is 2 inches thick. Which expression tells us how many books are in the stack? Be prepared to explain your reasoning.

  ○ $72 \cdot 2$          ○ $72 - 2$          ○ $2 \div 72$          ○ $72 \div 2$

3. Another stack of books is 43 inches tall. Each book is $\frac{1}{2}$-inch thick. Write an expression that represents the number of books in the stack.

## 1.3: All in Order

Your teacher will give you two sets of papers with division expressions.

1. Without computing, estimate the quotients in each set and order them from greatest to least. Be prepared to explain your reasoning.

  Pause here for a class discussion.

  Record the expressions in each set in order from the greatest value to the least.

  a. Set 1

  b. Set 2

2. Without computing, estimate the quotients and sort them into the following three groups. Be prepared to explain your reasoning.

  $30 \div \frac{1}{2}$          $9 \div 10$          $18 \div 19$          $15,000 \div 1,500,000$

  $30 \div 0.45$          $9 \div 10,000$          $18 \div 0.18$          $15,000 \div 14,500$

  ○ Close to 0                ○ Close to 1                ○ Much larger than 1

## Are you ready for more?

Write 10 expressions of the form 12÷? in a list ordered from least to greatest. Can you list expressions that have value near 1 without equaling 1? How close can you get to the value 1?

## Lesson 1 Summary

Here is a division expression: $60 \div 4$. In this division, we call 60 the *dividend* and 4 the *divisor*. The result of the division is the quotient. In this example, the quotient is 15, because $60 \div 4 = 15$.

We don't always have to make calculations to have a sense of what a quotient will be. We can reason about it by looking at the size of the dividend and the divisor. Let's look at some examples.

- In $100 \div 11$ and in $18 \div 2.9$ the dividend is larger than the divisor. $100 \div 11$ is very close to $99 \div 11$, which is 9. The quotient $18 \div 2.9$ is close to $18 \div 3$ or 6.

  In general, when a larger number is divided by a smaller number, the quotient is greater than 1.

- In $99 \div 101$ and in $7.5 \div 7.4$ the dividend and divisor are very close to each other. $99 \div 101$ is very close to $99 \div 100$, which is $\frac{99}{100}$ or 0.99. The quotient $7.5 \div 7.4$ is close to $7.5 \div 7.5$, which is 1.

  In general, when we divide two numbers that are nearly equal to each other, the quotient is close to 1.

- In $10 \div 101$ and in $50 \div 198$ the dividend is smaller than the divisor. $10 \div 101$ is very close to $10 \div 100$, which is $\frac{10}{100}$ or 0.1. The division $50 \div 198$ is close to $50 \div 200$, which is $\frac{1}{4}$ or 0.25.

  In general, when a smaller number is divided by a larger number, the quotient is less than 1.

# Lesson 1 Practice Problems

1. Order from smallest to largest:

    ○ Number of pennies in a stack that is 1 ft high

    ○ Number of books in a stack that is 1 ft high

    ○ Number of dollar bills in a stack that is 1 ft high

    ○ Number of slices of bread in a stack that is 1 ft high

2. Use each of the numbers 4, 40, and 4000 once to complete the sentences.

    a. The value of _____ ÷ 40.01 is close to 1.

    b. The value of _____ ÷ 40.01 is much less than 1.

    c. The value of _____ ÷ 40.01 is much greater than 1.

3. Without computing, decide whether the value of each expression is much smaller than 1, close to 1, or much greater than 1.

    a. $100 \div \frac{1}{1000}$

    b. $50\frac{1}{3} \div 50\frac{1}{4}$

    c. $4.7 \div 5.2$

    d. $2 \div 7335$

    e. $2,000,001 \div 9$

    f. $0.002 \div 2,000$

4. A rocking horse has a weight limit of 60 pounds.

   a. What percentage of the weight limit is 33 pounds?

   b. What percentage of the weight limit is 114 pounds?

   c. What weight is 95% of the limit?

   (From Unit 3, Lesson 16.)

5. Compare using >, =, or <.

   a. 0.7 _____ 0.70

   b. $0.03 + \frac{6}{10}$ _____ $0.30 + \frac{6}{100}$

   c. 0.9 _____ 0.12

   (From Unit 3, Lesson 15.)

iM KH

6. Diego has 90 songs on his playlist. How many songs are there for each genre?

    a. 40% rock

    b. 10% country

    c. 30% hip-hop

    d. The rest is electronica

(From Unit 3, Lesson 14.)

7. A garden hose emits 9 quarts of water in 6 seconds. At this rate:

    a. How long will it take the hose to emit 12 quarts?

    b. How much water does the hose emit in 10 seconds?

(From Unit 3, Lesson 8.)

# Lesson 2: Meanings of Division

Let's explore ways to think about division.

## 2.1: A Division Expression

Here is an expression: 20 ÷ 4.

What are some ways to think about this expression? Describe at least two meanings you think it could have. *There are 20 chiket players and 4 teams. how many players are oh each team? in eacr 6 team? there are 20 chikot players 4 payers per team how many teams arr thier*

## 2.2: Bags of Almonds

A baker has 12 pounds of almonds. She puts them in bags, so that each bag has the same weight.

Clare and Tyler drew diagrams and wrote equations to show how they were thinking about 12 ÷ 6.

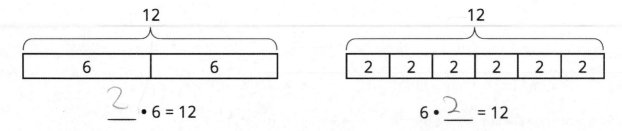

$$\underline{2} \cdot 6 = 12$$

Clare's diagram and equation

$$6 \cdot \underline{2} = 12$$

Tyler's diagram and equation

1. How do you think Clare and Tyler thought about 12 ÷ 6? Explain what each diagram and the parts of each equation could mean about the situation with the bags of almonds. Make sure to include the meaning of the missing number.

    Pause here for a class discussion.

iM KH

2. Explain what each division expression could mean about the situation with the bags of almonds. Then draw a diagram and write a multiplication equation to show how you are thinking about the expression.

a. $12 \div 4$

12 pounds of almounds and 4 bags. how many pounds go in each bag

b. $12 \div 2$

12

c. $12 \div \frac{1}{2}$

There are 12 pounds of Almounds and we pat ½ pound of Almonds in each bag how many bags of almounds will i have

**Are you ready for more?**

A loaf of bread is cut into slices.

1. If each slice is $\frac{1}{2}$ of a loaf, how many slices are there?

2. If each slice is $\frac{1}{5}$ of a loaf, how many slices are there?

3. What happens to the number of slices as each slice gets smaller?

4. What would dividing by 0 mean in this situation about slicing bread?

## Lesson 2 Summary

Suppose 24 bagels are being distributed into boxes. The expression $24 \div 3$ could be understood in two ways:

- 24 bagels are distributed equally into 3 boxes, as represented by this diagram:

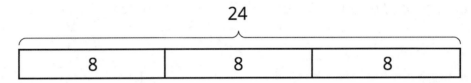

- 24 bagels are distributed into boxes, 3 bagels in each box, as represented by this diagram:

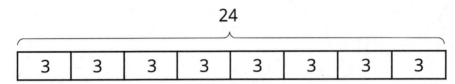

In both interpretations, the quotient is the same ($24 \div 3 = 8$), but it has different meanings in each case. In the first case, the 8 represents the number of bagels in each of the 3 boxes. In the second, it represents the number of boxes that were formed with 3 bagels in each box.

These two ways of seeing division are related to how 3, 8, and 24 are related in a multiplication. Both $3 \cdot 8$ and $8 \cdot 3$ equal 24.

- $3 \cdot 8 = 24$ can be read as "3 groups of 8 make 24."

- $8 \cdot 3 = 24$ can be read as "8 groups of 3 make 24."

If 3 and 24 are the only numbers given, the multiplication equations would be:
$$3 \cdot ? = 24$$
$$? \cdot 3 = 24$$

In both cases, the division $24 \div 3$ can be used to find the value of the "?" But now we see that it can be interpreted in more than one way, because the "?" can refer to *the size of a group* (as in "3 groups of what number make 24?"), or to *the number of groups* (as in "How many groups of 3 make 24?").

iM KH

# Lesson 2 Practice Problems

1. Twenty pounds of strawberries are being shared equally by a group of friends. The equation $20 \div 5 = 4$ represents the division of strawberries.

    a. If the 5 represents the number of people, what does the 4 represent?

    $4 =$ how many people / groups

    b. If the 5 represents the pounds of strawberries per person, what does the 4 represent?

    $4 =$ lbs. of strawberrys each get

2. A sixth-grade science club needs $180 to pay for the tickets to a science museum. All tickets cost the same amount.

    What could $180 \div 15$ mean in this situation? Describe two different possible meanings of this expression. Then, find the quotient and explain what it means in each case. I have $180 I have to buy 15 tikets how much does each cost.

    I have $180 each cost $15 how many can I buy.

3. Write a multiplication equation that corresponds to each division equation.

    a. $10 \div 5 = ?$

    b. $4.5 \div 3 = ?$

    c. $\frac{1}{2} \div 4 = ?$

4. Write a division or multiplication equation that represents each situation. Use a "?" for the unknown quantity.

    a. 2.5 gallons of water are poured into 5 equally sized bottles. How much water is in each bottle?

    b. A large bucket of 200 golf balls is divided into 4 smaller buckets. How many golf balls are in each small bucket?

    c. Sixteen socks are put into pairs. How many pairs are there?

5. Find a value for $a$ that makes each statement true.

    a. $a \div 6$ is greater than 1

    b. $a \div 6$ is equal to 1

    c. $a \div 6$ is less than 1

    d. $a \div 6$ is equal to a whole number

(From Unit 4, Lesson 1.)

6. Complete the table. Write each percentage as a percent of 1.

| fraction | decimal | percentage |
|----------|---------|------------|
| $\frac{1}{4}$ | 0.25 | 25% of 1 |
|  | 0.1 |  |
|  |  | 75% of 1 |
| $\frac{1}{5}$ |  |  |
|  | 1.5 |  |
|  |  | 140% of 1 |

(From Unit 3, Lesson 14.)

7. Jada walks at a speed of 3 miles per hour. Elena walks at a speed of 2.8 miles per hour. If they both begin walking along a walking trail at the same time, how much farther will Jada walk after 3 hours? Explain your reasoning.

(From Unit 3, Lesson 8.)

iM KH

# Lesson 3: Interpreting Division Situations

Let's explore situations that involve division.

## 3.1: Dot Image: Properties of Multiplication

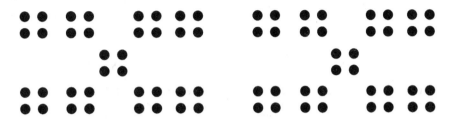

## 3.2: Homemade Jams

Draw a diagram, and write a multiplication equation to represent each situation. Then answer the question.

1. Mai had 4 jars. In each jar, she put $2\frac{1}{4}$ cups of homemade blueberry jam. Altogether, how many cups of jam are in the jars?

2. Priya filled 5 jars, using a total of $7\frac{1}{2}$ cups of strawberry jam. How many cups of jam are in each jar?

3. Han had some jars. He put $\frac{3}{4}$ cup of grape jam in each jar, using a total of $6\frac{3}{4}$ cups. How many jars did he fill?

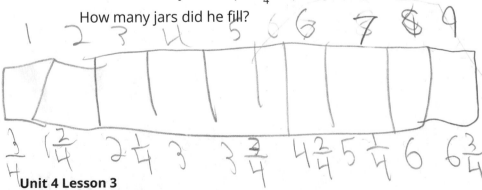

## 3.3: Making Granola

1. Consider the problem: To make 1 batch of granola, Kiran needs 26 ounces of oats. The only measuring tool he has is a 4-ounce scoop. How many scoops will it take to measure 26 ounces of oats?

   a. Will the answer be (more than 1) or less than 1?

   b. Write a multiplication equation and a division equation that represent this situation. Use "?" to represent the unknown quantity.

   c. Find the unknown quantity. If you get stuck, consider drawing a diagram.

   $$26 \div 4 = 6\tfrac{1}{2}$$

2. The recipe calls for 14 ounces of mixed nuts. To get that amount, Kiran uses 4 bags of mixed nuts.

   a. Write a mathematical question that might be asked about this situation.

   b. What might the equation $14 \div 4 = \;?$ represent in Kiran's situation?

   c. Find the quotient. Show your reasoning. If you get stuck, consider drawing a diagram.

## Lesson 3 Summary

If a situation involves equal-sized groups, it is helpful to make sense of it in terms of the number of groups, the size of each group, and the total amount. Here are three examples to help us better understand such situations.

- Suppose we have 3 bottles with $6\frac{1}{2}$ ounces of water in each, and the total amount of water is not given. Here we have 3 groups, $6\frac{1}{2}$ ounces in each group, and an unknown total, as shown in this diagram:

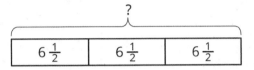

We can express this situation as a multiplication problem. The unknown is the product, so we can simply multiply the 2 known numbers to find it.

$$3 \cdot 6\frac{1}{2} = ?$$

- Next, suppose we have 20 ounces of water to fill 6 equal-sized bottles, and the amount in each bottle is not given. Here we have 6 groups, an unknown amount in each, and a total of 20. We can represent it like this:

$$20$$

| ? | ? | ? | ? | ? | ? |

This situation can also be expressed using multiplication, but the unknown is a factor, rather than the product:

$$6 \cdot ? = 20$$

To find the unknown, we cannot simply multiply, but we can think of it as a division problem:

$$20 \div 6 = ?$$

- Now, suppose we have 40 ounces of water to pour into bottles, 12 ounces in each bottle, but the number of bottles is not given. Here we have an unknown number of groups, 12 in each group, and a total of 40.

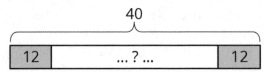

Again, we can think of this in terms of multiplication, with a different factor being the unknown:

$$? \cdot 12 = 40$$

Likewise, we can use division to find the unknown:

$$40 \div 12 = ?$$

Whenever we have a multiplication situation, one factor tells us *how many groups* there are, and the other factor tells us *how much is in each group*.

Sometimes we want to find the total. Sometimes we want to find how many groups there are. Sometimes we want to find how much is in each group. Anytime we want to find out how many groups there are or how much is in each group, we can represent the situation using division.

iM KH

# Lesson 3 Practice Problems

1. Write a multiplication equation and a division equation that this diagram could represent.

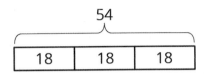

2. Consider the problem: Mai has $36 to spend on movie tickets. Each movie ticket costs $4.50. How many tickets can she buy?

   a. Write a multiplication equation and a division equation to represent this situation.

   b. Find the answer. Draw a diagram, if needed.

   c. Use the multiplication equation to check your answer.

3. Kiran said that this diagram can show the solution to $16 \div 8 = ?$ or $16 \div 2 = ?$, depending on how we think about the equations and the "?".

   Explain or show how Kiran is correct.

   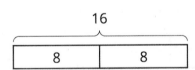

4. Write a sentence describing a situation that could be represented by the equation $4 \div 1\frac{1}{3} = ?$.

   (From Unit 4, Lesson 2.)

5. Noah said, "When you divide a number by a second number, the result will always be smaller than the first number."

Jada said, "I think the result could be larger or smaller, depending on the numbers."

Do you agree with either of them? Explain or show your reasoning.

(From Unit 4, Lesson 1.)

6. Mini muffins cost $3.00 per dozen.

   ○ Andre says, "I have $2.00, so I can afford 8 muffins."
   ○ Elena says, "I want to get 16 muffins, so I'll need to pay $4.00."

Do you agree with either of them? Explain your reasoning.

(From Unit 3, Lesson 7.)

7. A family has a monthly budget of $2,400. How much money is spent on each category?

   a. 44% is spent on housing.

   b. 23% is spent on food.

   c. 6% is spent on clothing.

   d. 17% is spent on transportation.

   e. The rest is put into savings.

(From Unit 3, Lesson 15.)

iM KH

# Lesson 4: How Many Groups? (Part 1)

Let's play with blocks and diagrams to think about division with fractions.

## 4.1: Equal-sized Groups

Write a multiplication equation and a division equation for each sentence or diagram.

1. Eight $5 bills are worth $40.

2. There are 9 thirds in 3 ones.

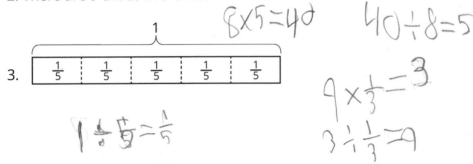

3.

$8 \times 5 = 40$

$40 \div 8 = 5$

$9 \times \frac{1}{3} = 3$

$3 \div \frac{1}{3} = 9$

$1 \div \frac{1}{5} = \frac{1}{5}$

## 4.2: Reasoning with Pattern Blocks

Your teacher will give you pattern blocks as shown here. Use them to answer the questions.

1. If a hexagon represents 1 whole, what fraction does each of the following shapes represent? Be prepared to show or explain your reasoning.

   ○ 1 triangle $\frac{1}{6}$

   ○ 4 triangles $\frac{4}{6}$

   ○ 1 hexagon and 1 trapezoid $\frac{8}{6}$

   ○ 1 rhombus $\frac{1}{3}$

   ○ 3 rhombuses 1

   ○ 1 trapezoid $\frac{1}{2}$

   ○ 2 hexagons 1

2. Here are Elena's diagrams for $2 \cdot \frac{1}{2} = 1$ and $6 \cdot \frac{1}{3} = 2$. Do you think these diagrams represent the equations? Explain or show your reasoning.

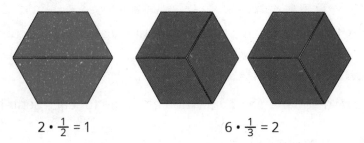

$2 \cdot \frac{1}{2} = 1$            $6 \cdot \frac{1}{3} = 2$

3. Use pattern blocks to represent each multiplication equation. Remember that a hexagon represents 1 whole.

   a. $3 \cdot \frac{1}{6} = \frac{1}{2}$

   b. $2 \cdot \frac{3}{2} = 3$

4. Answer the questions. If you get stuck, consider using pattern blocks.

   a. How many $\frac{1}{2}$s are in 4?   8

   b. How many $\frac{2}{3}$s are in 2?   3

   c. How many $\frac{1}{6}$s are in $1\frac{1}{2}$?   9

iM KH

## Lesson 4 Summary

Some problems that involve equal-sized groups also involve fractions. Here is an example: "How many $\frac{1}{6}$ are in 2?" We can express this question with multiplication and division equations.

$$? \cdot \frac{1}{6} = 2$$

$$2 \div \frac{1}{6} = ?$$

Pattern-block diagrams can help us make sense of such problems. Here is a set of pattern blocks.

If the hexagon represents 1 whole, then a triangle must represent $\frac{1}{6}$, because 6 triangles make 1 hexagon. We can use the triangle to represent the $\frac{1}{6}$ in the problem.

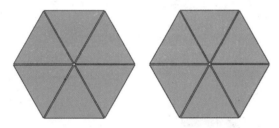

Twelve triangles make 2 hexagons, which means there are 12 groups of $\frac{1}{6}$ in 2.

If we write the 12 in the place of the "?" in the original equations, we have:

$$12 \cdot \frac{1}{6} = 2$$

$$2 \div \frac{1}{6} = 12$$

# Lesson 4 Practice Problems

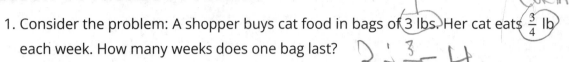

1. Consider the problem: A shopper buys cat food in bags of 3 lbs. Her cat eats $\frac{3}{4}$ lb each week. How many weeks does one bag last?

   $3 \div \frac{3}{4} = 4$

   a. Draw a diagram to represent the situation and label your diagram so it can be followed by others. Answer the question.

   b. Write a multiplication or division equation to represent the situation.

   c. Multiply your answer in the first question (the number of weeks) by $\frac{3}{4}$. Did you get 3 as a result? If not, revise your previous work.

2. Use the diagram to answer the question: How many $\frac{1}{3}$s are in $1\frac{2}{3}$? The hexagon represents 1 whole. Explain or show your reasoning.

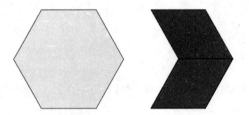

3. Which question can be represented by the equation $? \cdot \frac{1}{8} = 3$?

   A. How many 3s are in $\frac{1}{8}$?

   B. What is 3 groups of $\frac{1}{8}$?

   C. How many $\frac{1}{8}$s are in 3?

   D. What is $\frac{1}{8}$ of 3?

iM KH

4. Write two division equations for each multiplication equation.

    a. $15 \cdot \frac{2}{5} = 6$

    b. $6 \cdot \frac{4}{3} = 8$

    c. $16 \cdot \frac{7}{8} = 14$

5. Noah and his friends are going to an amusement park. The total cost of admission for 8 students is $100, and all students share the cost equally. Noah brought $13 for his ticket. Did he bring enough money to get into the park? Explain your reasoning.

(From Unit 4, Lesson 2.)

6. Write a division expression with a quotient that is:

    a. greater than $8 \div 0.001$

    b. less than $8 \div 0.001$

    c. between $8 \div 0.001$ and $8 \div \frac{1}{10}$

(From Unit 4, Lesson 1.)

7. Find each unknown number.

    a. 12 is 150% of what number?

    b. 5 is 50% of what number?

    c. 10% of what number is 300?

    d. 5% of what number is 72?

    e. 20 is 80% of what number?

(From Unit 3, Lesson 14.)

# Lesson 5: How Many Groups? (Part 2)

Let's use blocks and diagrams to understand more about division with fractions.

## 5.1: Reasoning with Fraction Strips

Write a fraction or whole number as an answer for each question. If you get stuck, use the fraction strips. Be prepared to share your reasoning.

1. How many $\frac{1}{2}$s are in 2?    4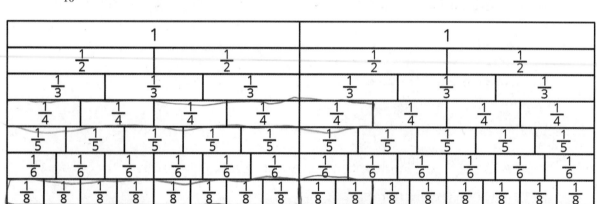

2. How many $\frac{1}{5}$s are in 3?    15

3. How many $\frac{1}{8}$s are in $1\frac{1}{4}$?    10

4. $1 \div \frac{2}{6} = ?$

5. $2 \div \frac{2}{9} = ?$    9

6. $4 \div \frac{2}{10} = ?$

| 1 | | | | | | 1 | | | | | |
|---|---|---|---|---|---|---|---|---|---|---|---|
| $\frac{1}{2}$ | | | $\frac{1}{2}$ | | | $\frac{1}{2}$ | | | $\frac{1}{2}$ | | |
| $\frac{1}{3}$ | | $\frac{1}{3}$ | | $\frac{1}{3}$ | | $\frac{1}{3}$ | | $\frac{1}{3}$ | | $\frac{1}{3}$ | |
| $\frac{1}{4}$ | | $\frac{1}{4}$ | | $\frac{1}{4}$ | | $\frac{1}{4}$ | $\frac{1}{4}$ | | $\frac{1}{4}$ | | $\frac{1}{4}$ |
| $\frac{1}{5}$ | $\frac{1}{5}$ | $\frac{1}{5}$ | $\frac{1}{5}$ | $\frac{1}{5}$ | $\frac{1}{5}$ | $\frac{1}{5}$ | $\frac{1}{5}$ | $\frac{1}{5}$ | $\frac{1}{5}$ | | |
| $\frac{1}{6}$ | $\frac{1}{6}$ | $\frac{1}{6}$ | $\frac{1}{6}$ | $\frac{1}{6}$ | $\frac{1}{6}$ | $\frac{1}{6}$ | $\frac{1}{6}$ | $\frac{1}{6}$ | $\frac{1}{6}$ | $\frac{1}{6}$ | $\frac{1}{6}$ |
| $\frac{1}{8}$ | $\frac{1}{8}$ | $\frac{1}{8}$ | $\frac{1}{8}$ | $\frac{1}{8}$ | $\frac{1}{8}$ | $\frac{1}{8}$ | $\frac{1}{8}$ | $\frac{1}{8}$ | $\frac{1}{8}$ | $\frac{1}{8}$ | $\frac{1}{8}$ |
| $\frac{1}{9}$ | $\frac{1}{9}$ | $\frac{1}{9}$ | $\frac{1}{9}$ | $\frac{1}{9}$ | $\frac{1}{9}$ | $\frac{1}{9}$ | $\frac{1}{9}$ | $\frac{1}{9}$ | $\frac{1}{9}$ | $\frac{1}{9}$ | $\frac{1}{9}$ |

iM KH

# 5.2: More Reasoning with Pattern Blocks

Your teacher will give you pattern blocks. Use them to answer the questions.

1. If the trapezoid represents 1 whole, what do each of the other shapes represent? Be prepared to show or explain your reasoning.

2. Use pattern blocks to represent each multiplication equation. Use the trapezoid to represent 1 whole.

   a. $3 \cdot \frac{1}{3} = 1$

   b. $3 \cdot \frac{2}{3} = 2$

3. Diego and Jada were asked "How many rhombuses are in a trapezoid?"

   ○ Diego says, "$1\frac{1}{3}$. If I put 1 rhombus on a trapezoid, the leftover shape is a triangle, which is $\frac{1}{3}$ of the trapezoid."

   ○ Jada says, "I think it's $1\frac{1}{2}$. Since we want to find out 'how many rhombuses,' we should compare the leftover triangle to a rhombus. A triangle is $\frac{1}{2}$ of a rhombus."

   Do you agree with either of them? Explain or show your reasoning.

4. Select **all** the equations that can be used to answer the question: "How many rhombuses are in a trapezoid?"

○ $\frac{2}{3} \div ? = 1$        ○ $1 \div \frac{2}{3} = ?$        ○ $? \div \frac{2}{3} = 1$

○ $? \cdot \frac{2}{3} = 1$        ○ $1 \cdot \frac{2}{3} = ?$

## 5.3: Drawing Diagrams to Show Equal-sized Groups

For each situation, draw a diagram for the relationship of the quantities to help you answer the question. Then write a multiplication equation or a division equation for the relationship. Be prepared to share your reasoning.

1. The distance around a park is $\frac{3}{2}$ miles. Noah rode his bicycle around the park for a total of 3 miles. How many times around the park did he ride?

2. You need $\frac{3}{4}$ yard of ribbon for one gift box. You have 3 yards of ribbon. How many gift boxes do you have ribbon for?

3. The water hose fills a bucket at $\frac{1}{3}$ gallon per minute. How many minutes does it take to fill a 2-gallon bucket?

### Are you ready for more?

How many heaping teaspoons are in a heaping tablespoon? How would the answer depend on the shape of the spoons?

iM KH

## Lesson 5 Summary

Suppose one batch of cookies requires $\frac{2}{3}$ cup flour. How many batches can be made with 4 cups of flour?

We can think of the question as being: "How many $\frac{2}{3}$ are in 4?" and represent it using multiplication and division equations.

$$? \cdot \frac{2}{3} = 4$$

$$4 \div \frac{2}{3} = ?$$

Let's use pattern blocks to visualize the situation and say that a hexagon is 1 whole.

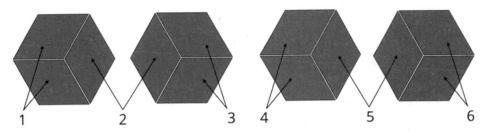

Since 3 rhombuses make a hexagon, 1 rhombus represents $\frac{1}{3}$ and 2 rhombuses represent $\frac{2}{3}$. We can see that 6 pairs of rhombuses make 4 hexagons, so there are 6 groups of $\frac{2}{3}$ in 4.

Other kinds of diagrams can also help us reason about equal-sized groups involving fractions. This example shows how we might reason about the same question from above: "How many $\frac{2}{3}$-cups are in 4 cups?"

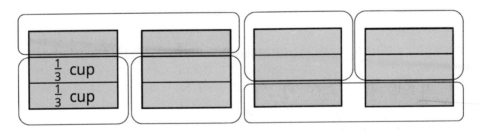

We can see each "cup" partitioned into thirds, and that there are 6 groups of $\frac{2}{3}$-cup in 4 cups. In both diagrams, we see that the unknown value (or the "?" in the equations) is 6. So we can now write:

$$6 \cdot \frac{2}{3} = 4$$

$$4 \div \frac{2}{3} = 6$$

# Lesson 5 Practice Problems

1. Use the tape diagram to find the value of $\frac{1}{2} \div \frac{1}{3}$. Show your reasoning.

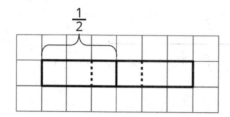

2. What is the value of $\frac{1}{2} \div \frac{1}{3}$? Use pattern blocks to represent and find this value. The yellow hexagon represents 1 whole. Explain or show your reasoning.

3. Use a standard inch ruler to answer each question. Then, write a multiplication equation and a division equation that answer the question.

   a. How many $\frac{1}{2}$s are in 7?

   b. How many $\frac{3}{8}$s are in 6?

   c. How many $\frac{5}{16}$s are in $1\frac{7}{8}$?

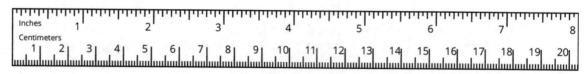

4. Use the tape diagram to answer the question: How many $\frac{2}{5}$s are in $1\frac{1}{2}$? Show your reasoning.

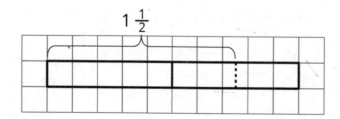

iM KH

5. Write a multiplication equation and a division equation to represent each sentence or diagram.

   a. There are 12 fourths in 3.

   b.

| 2 | | | |
|---|---|---|---|
| $\frac{1}{2}$ | $\frac{1}{2}$ | $\frac{1}{2}$ | $\frac{1}{2}$ |

   c. How many $\frac{2}{3}$s are in 6?

   d.

| 2 | | | | |
|---|---|---|---|---|
| $\frac{2}{5}$ | $\frac{2}{5}$ | $\frac{2}{5}$ | $\frac{2}{5}$ | $\frac{2}{5}$ |

   (From Unit 4, Lesson 4.)

6. At a farmer's market, two vendors sell fresh milk. One vendor sells 2 liters for $3.80, and another vendor sells 1.5 liters for $2.70. Which is the better deal? Explain your reasoning.

   (From Unit 3, Lesson 5.)

7. A recipe uses 5 cups of flour for every 2 cups of sugar.

   a. How much sugar is used for 1 cup of flour?

   b. How much flour is used for 1 cup of sugar?

   c. How much flour is used with 7 cups of sugar?

   d. How much sugar is used with 6 cups of flour?

   (From Unit 3, Lesson 6.)

# Lesson 6: Using Diagrams to Find the Number of Groups

Let's draw tape diagrams to think about division with fractions.

## 6.1: How Many of These in That?

1. We can think of the division expression $10 \div 2\frac{1}{2}$ as the question: "How many groups of $2\frac{1}{2}$ are in 10?" Complete the tape diagram to represent this question. Then find the answer.

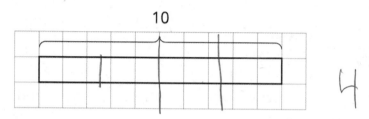

4

2. Complete the tape diagram to represent the question: "How many groups of 2 are in 7?" Then find the answer.

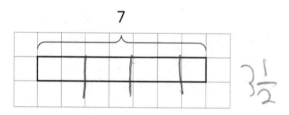

$3\frac{1}{2}$

# 6.2: Representing Groups of Fractions with Tape Diagrams

To make sense of the question "How many $\frac{2}{3}$s are in 1?," Andre wrote equations and drew a tape diagram.

$$? \cdot \frac{2}{3} = 1$$

$$1 \div \frac{2}{3} = ?$$

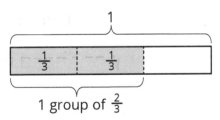

1 group of $\frac{2}{3}$

1. In an earlier task, we used pattern blocks to help us solve the equation $1 \div \frac{2}{3} = ?$. Explain how Andre's tape diagram can also help us solve the equation.

2. Write a multiplication equation and a division equation for each question. Then, draw a tape diagram and find the answer.

   $? \times \frac{3}{4} = 1 \frac{1}{3}$

   $1 \div \frac{3}{4} = ?$

   a. How many $\frac{3}{4}$s are in 1?

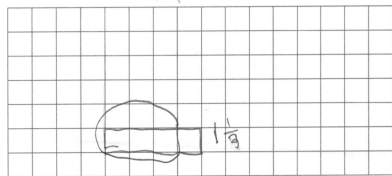

   b. How many $\frac{2}{3}$s are in 3?

$3 \div \frac{2}{3} =$

$\frac{2}{3} \times ? = 3$

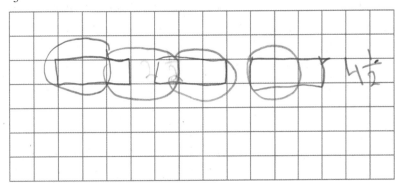

c. How many $\frac{3}{2}$s are in 5?

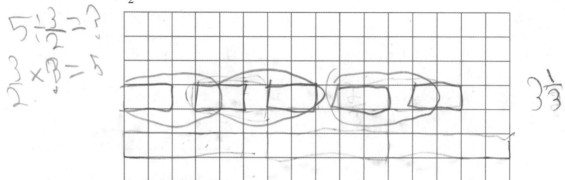

$5 \div \frac{3}{2} = ?$

$\frac{3}{2} \times \boxed{?} = 5$

$3\frac{1}{3}$

## 6.3: Finding Number of Groups

1. Write a multiplication equation or a division equation for each question. Then, find the answer and explain or show your reasoning.

   a. How many $\frac{3}{8}$-inch thick books make a stack that is 6 inches tall?

   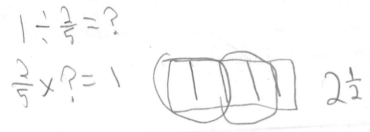

   $1 \div \frac{2}{5} = ?$

   $\frac{2}{5} \times ? = 1$

   $2\frac{1}{2}$

   b. How many groups of $\frac{1}{2}$ pound are in $2\frac{3}{4}$ pounds?

2. Write a question that can be represented by the division equation $5 \div 1\frac{1}{2} = ?$. Then, find the answer and explain or show your reasoning.

iM KH

## Lesson 6 Summary

A baker used 2 kilograms of flour to make several batches of a pastry recipe. The recipe called for $\frac{2}{5}$ kilogram of flour per batch. How many batches did she make?

We can think of the question as: "How many groups of $\frac{2}{5}$ kilogram make 2 kilograms?" and represent that question with the equations:

$$? \cdot \frac{2}{5} = 2$$

$$2 \div \frac{2}{5} = ?$$

To help us make sense of the question, we can draw a tape diagram. This diagram shows 2 whole kilograms, with each kilogram partitioned into fifths.

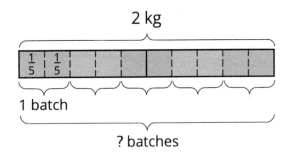

We can see there are 5 groups of $\frac{2}{5}$ in 2. Multiplying 5 and $\frac{2}{5}$ allows us to check this answer: $5 \cdot \frac{2}{5} = \frac{10}{5}$ and $\frac{10}{5} = 2$, so the answer is correct.

Notice the number of groups that result from $2 \div \frac{2}{5}$ is a whole number. Sometimes the number of groups we find from dividing may not be a whole number. Here is an example:

Suppose one serving of rice is $\frac{3}{4}$ cup. How many servings are there in $3\frac{1}{2}$ cups?

$$? \cdot \frac{3}{4} = 3\frac{1}{2}$$

$$3\frac{1}{2} \div \frac{3}{4} = ?$$

Looking at the diagram, we can see there are 4 full groups of $\frac{3}{4}$, plus 2 fourths. If 3 fourths make a whole group, then 2 fourths make $\frac{2}{3}$ of a group. So the number of servings (the "?" in each equation) is $4\frac{2}{3}$. We can check this by multiplying $4\frac{2}{3}$ and $\frac{3}{4}$.

$4\frac{2}{3} \cdot \frac{3}{4} = \frac{14}{3} \cdot \frac{3}{4}$, and $\frac{14}{3} \cdot \frac{3}{4} = \frac{14}{4}$, which is indeed equivalent to $3\frac{1}{2}$.

## Lesson 6 Practice Problems

1. We can think of $3 \div \frac{1}{4}$ as the question "How many groups of $\frac{1}{4}$ are in 3?" Draw a tape diagram to represent this question. Then find the answer.

2. Describe how to draw a tape diagram to represent and answer $3 \div \frac{3}{5} = ?$ for a friend who was absent.

3. How many groups of $\frac{1}{2}$ day are in 1 week?

    a. Write a multiplication equation or a division equation to represent the question.

    b. Draw a tape diagram to show the relationship between the quantities and to answer the question. Use graph paper, if needed.

4. Diego said that the answer to the question "How many groups of $\frac{5}{6}$ are in 1?" is $\frac{6}{5}$ or $1\frac{1}{5}$. Do you agree with him? Explain or show your reasoning.

5. Select **all** the equations that can represent the question: "How many groups of $\frac{4}{5}$ are in 1?"

   A. $? \cdot 1 = \frac{4}{5}$

   B. $1 \cdot \frac{4}{5} = ?$

   C. $\frac{4}{5} \div 1 = ?$

   D. $? \cdot \frac{4}{5} = 1$

   E. $1 \div \frac{4}{5} = ?$

   (From Unit 4, Lesson 5.)

6. Calculate each percentage mentally.

   a. What is 10% of 70?

   b. What is 10% of 110?

   c. What is 25% of 160?

   d. What is 25% of 48?

   e. What is 50% of 90?

   f. What is 50% of 350?

   g. What is 75% of 300?

   h. What is 75% of 48?

   (From Unit 3, Lesson 14.)

# Lesson 7: What Fraction of a Group?

Let's think about dividing things into groups when we can't even make one whole group.

## 7.1: Estimating a Fraction of a Number

1. Estimate the quantities:

    a. What is $\frac{1}{3}$ of 7?

    b. What is $\frac{4}{5}$ of $9\frac{2}{3}$?

    c. What is $2\frac{4}{7}$ of $10\frac{1}{9}$?

2. Write a multiplication expression for each of the previous questions.

## 7.2: Fractions of Ropes

Here is a diagram that shows four ropes of different lengths.

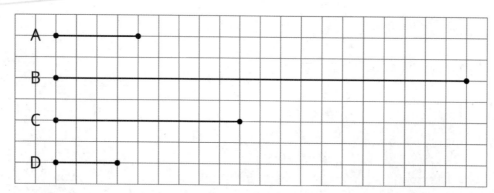

1. Complete each sentence comparing the lengths of the ropes. Then, use the measurements shown on the grid to write a multiplication equation and a division equation for each comparison.

    a. Rope B is _____ times as long as Rope A.

    b. Rope C is _____ times as long as Rope A.

    c. Rope D is _____ times as long as Rope A.

iM KH

2. Each equation can be used to answer a question about Ropes C and D. What could each question be?

   a. $? \cdot 3 = 9$ and $9 \div 3 = ?$

   b. $? \cdot 9 = 3$ and $3 \div 9 = ?$

## 7.3: Fractional Batches of Ice Cream

One batch of an ice cream recipe uses 9 cups of milk. A chef makes different amounts of ice cream on different days. Here are the amounts of milk she used:

- Monday: 12 cups
- Tuesday: $22\frac{1}{2}$ cups

- Thursday: 6 cups
- Friday: $7\frac{1}{2}$ cups

1. How many batches of ice cream did she make on these days? For each day, write a division equation, draw a tape diagram, and find the answer.

   a. Monday

   b. Tuesday

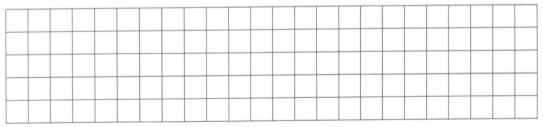

2. What fraction of a batch of ice cream did she make on these days? For each day, write a division equation, draw a tape diagram, and find the answer.

   a. Thursday

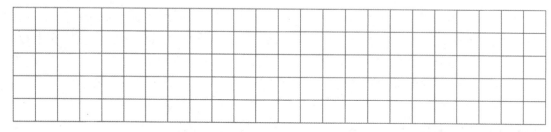

   b. Friday

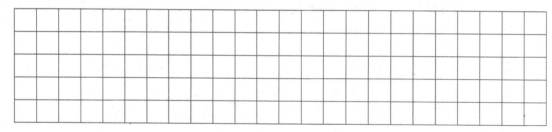

3. For each question, write a division equation, draw a tape diagram, and find the answer.

   a. What fraction of 9 is 3?

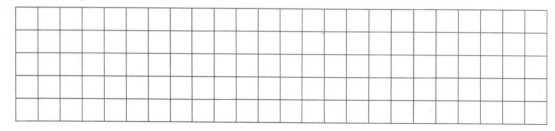

   b. What fraction of 5 is $\frac{1}{2}$?

iM KH

## Lesson 7 Summary

It is natural to think about groups when we have more than one group, but we can also have a *fraction of a group*.

To find the amount in a fraction of a group, we can multiply the fraction by the amount in the whole group. If a bag of rice weighs 5 kg, $\frac{3}{4}$ of a bag would weigh $(\frac{3}{4} \cdot 5)$ kg.

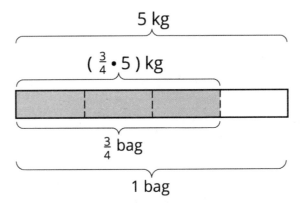

Sometimes we need to find what fraction of a group an amount is. Suppose a full bag of flour weighs 6 kg. A chef used 3 kg of flour. What fraction of a full bag was used? In other words, what fraction of 6 kg is 3 kg?

This question can be represented by a multiplication equation and a division equation, as well as by a diagram.

$$? \cdot 6 = 3$$
$$3 \div 6 = ?$$

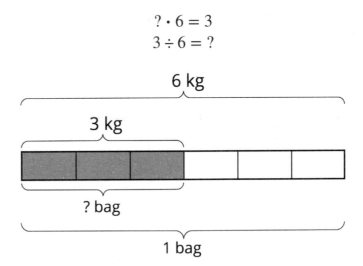

We can see from the diagram that 3 is $\frac{1}{2}$ of 6, and we can check this answer by multiplying: $\frac{1}{2} \cdot 6 = 3$.

In *any* situation where we want to know what fraction one number is of another number, we can write a division equation to help us find the answer.

For example, "What fraction of 3 is $2\frac{1}{4}$?" can be expressed as $? \cdot 3 = 2\frac{1}{4}$, which can also be written as $2\frac{1}{4} \div 3 = ?$.

The answer to "What is $2\frac{1}{4} \div 3$?" is also the answer to the original question.

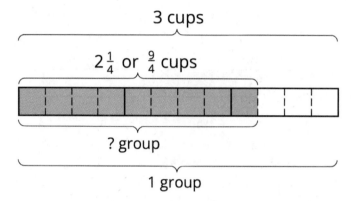

The diagram shows that 3 wholes contain 12 fourths, and $2\frac{1}{4}$ contains 9 fourths, so the answer to this question is $\frac{9}{12}$, which is equivalent to $\frac{3}{4}$.

We can use diagrams to help us solve other division problems that require finding a fraction of a group. For example, here is a diagram to help us answer the question: "What fraction of $\frac{9}{4}$ is $\frac{3}{2}$?," which can be written as $\frac{3}{2} \div \frac{9}{4} = ?$.

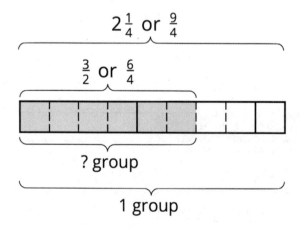

We can see that the quotient is $\frac{6}{9}$, which is equivalent to $\frac{2}{3}$. To check this, let's multiply. $\frac{2}{3} \cdot \frac{9}{4} = \frac{18}{12}$, and $\frac{18}{12}$ is, indeed, equal to $\frac{3}{2}$.

# Lesson 7 Practice Problems

1. A recipe calls for $\frac{1}{2}$ lb of flour for 1 batch. How many batches can be made with each of these amounts?

    a. 1 lb

    b. $\frac{3}{4}$ lb

    c. $\frac{1}{4}$ lb

2. Whiskers the cat weighs $2\frac{2}{3}$ kg. Piglio weighs 4 kg. For each question, write a multiplication equation and a division equation, decide whether the answer is greater than 1 or less than 1, and then find the answer.

    a. How many times as heavy as Piglio is Whiskers?

    b. How many times as heavy as Whiskers is Piglio?

3. Andre is walking from his home to a festival that is $1\frac{5}{8}$ kilometers away. He walks $\frac{1}{3}$ kilometer and then takes a quick rest. Which question can be represented by the equation $? \cdot 1\frac{5}{8} = \frac{1}{3}$ in this situation?

    A. What fraction of the trip has Andre completed?

    B. What fraction of the trip is left?

    C. How many more kilometers does Andre have to walk to get to the festival?

    D. How many kilometers is it from home to the festival and back home?

4. Draw a tape diagram to represent the question: What fraction of $2\frac{1}{2}$ is $\frac{4}{5}$? Then find the answer.

5. How many groups of $\frac{3}{4}$ are in each of these quantities?

   a. $\frac{11}{4}$

   b. $6\frac{1}{2}$

(From Unit 4, Lesson 6.)

6. Which question can be represented by the equation $4 \div \frac{2}{7} = ?$

   A. What is 4 groups of $\frac{2}{7}$?

   B. How many $\frac{2}{7}$s are in 4?

   C. What is $\frac{2}{7}$ of 4?

   D. How many 4s are in $\frac{2}{7}$?

(From Unit 4, Lesson 4.)

iM KH

# Lesson 8: How Much in Each Group? (Part 1)

Let's look at division problems that help us find the size of one group.

## 8.1: Inventing a Situation

1. Think of a situation with a question that can be represented by the equation $12 \div \frac{2}{3} = ?$ Describe the situation and the question.

2. Trade descriptions with your partner, and answer your partner's question.

## 8.2: How Much in One Batch?

To make 5 batches of cookies, 10 cups of flour are required. Consider the question: How many cups of flour does each batch require?

We can write equations and draw a diagram to represent this situation.

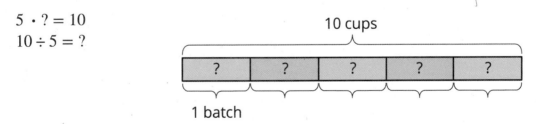

$$5 \cdot ? = 10$$
$$10 \div 5 = ?$$

This helps us see that each batch requires 2 cups of flour.

For each question, write a multiplication equation and a division equation, draw a diagram, and find the answer.

1. To make 4 batches of cupcakes, it takes 6 cups of flour. How many cups of flour are needed for 1 batch?

$$6 \div 4 = ?$$

2. To make $\frac{1}{2}$ batch of rolls, it takes $\frac{5}{4}$ cups of flour. How many cups of flour are needed for 1 batch?

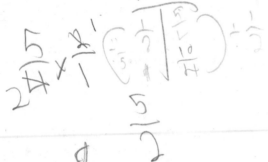

3. Two cups of flour make $\frac{2}{3}$ batch of bread. How many cups of flour make 1 batch?

$$\frac{2}{1} \div \frac{2}{3}$$

$$\frac{2}{1} \times \frac{3}{2} = \frac{3}{1} = 3$$

iM KH

# 8.3: One Container and One Section of Highway

Here are three tape diagrams that represent situations about filling containers of water.

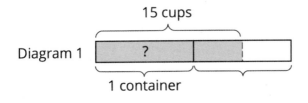

15 cups

Diagram 1

1 container

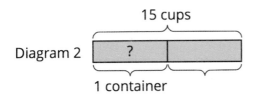

15 cups

Diagram 2

1 container

15 cups

Diagram 3

?

1 container

Match each situation to a diagram and use the diagram to help you answer the question. Then, write a multiplication equation and a division equation to represent the situation.

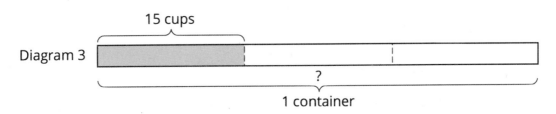

1. Tyler poured a total of 15 cups of water into 2 equal-sized bottles and filled each bottle. How much water was in each bottle?

$7\frac{1}{2}$

2. Kiran poured a total of 15 cups of water into equal-sized pitchers and filled $1\frac{1}{2}$ pitchers. How much water was in the full pitcher?

$\frac{15}{1} \times \frac{2}{3} = \frac{10}{1} = 10$

3. It takes 15 cups of water to fill $\frac{1}{3}$ pail. How much water is needed to fill 1 pail?

45

Here are tape diagrams that represent situations about cleaning sections of highway.

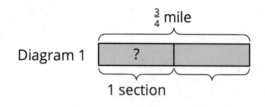

Diagram 1

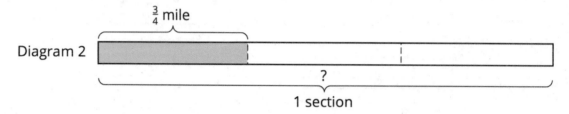

Diagram 2

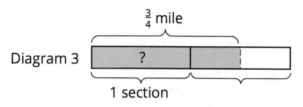

Diagram 3

Match each situation to a diagram and use the diagram to help you answer the question. Then, write a multiplication equation and a division equation to represent the situation.

4. Priya's class has adopted two equal sections of a highway to keep clean. The combined length is $\frac{3}{4}$ of a mile. How long is each section?

5. Lin's class has also adopted some sections of highway to keep clean. If $1\frac{1}{2}$ sections are $\frac{3}{4}$ mile long, how long is each section?

6. A school has adopted a section of highway to keep clean. If $\frac{1}{3}$ of the section is $\frac{3}{4}$ mile long, how long is the section?

iM KH

## Are you ready for more?

To make a Cantor ternary set:

- Start with a tape diagram of length 1 unit. This is step 1.
- Color in the middle third of the tape diagram. This is step 2.
- Do the same to each remaining segment that is not colored in. This is step 3.
- Keep repeating this process.

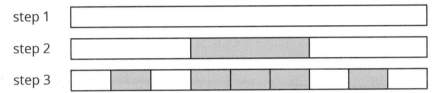

1. How much of the diagram is colored in after step 2? Step 3? Step 10?

2. If you continue this process, how much of the tape diagram will you color?

3. Can you think of a different process that will give you a similar result? For example, color the first fifth instead of the middle third of each strip.

## Lesson 8 Summary

Sometimes we know the amount for *multiple* groups, but we don't know how much is in one group. We can use division to find out.

For example, if 5 people share $8\frac{1}{2}$ pounds of cherries equally, how many pounds of cherries does each person get?

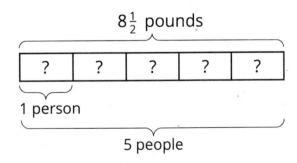

We can represent this situation with a multiplication equation and a division equation:

$$5 \cdot ? = 8\frac{1}{2}$$

$$8\frac{1}{2} \div 5 = ?$$

$8\frac{1}{2} \div 5$ can be written as $\frac{17}{2} \div 5$. Dividing by 5 is equivalent to multiplying by $\frac{1}{5}$, and $\frac{17}{2} \cdot \frac{1}{5} = \frac{17}{10}$. This means each person gets $1\frac{7}{10}$ pounds.

Other times, we know the amount for *a fraction* of a group, but we don't know the size of one whole group. We can also use division to find out.

For example, Jada poured 5 cups of iced tea in a pitcher and filled $\frac{2}{3}$ of the pitcher. How many cups of iced tea fill the entire pitcher?

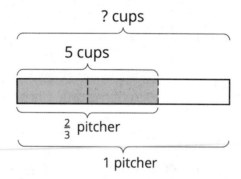

We can represent this situation with a multiplication equation and a division equation:

$$\frac{2}{3} \cdot ? = 5$$

$$5 \div \frac{2}{3} = ?$$

The diagram can help us reason about the answer. If $\frac{2}{3}$ of a pitcher is 5 cups, then $\frac{1}{3}$ of a pitcher is half of 5, which is $\frac{5}{2}$. Because there are 3 thirds in 1 whole, there would be $(3 \cdot \frac{5}{2})$ or $\frac{15}{2}$ cups in one whole pitcher. We can check our answer by multiplying: $\frac{2}{3} \cdot \frac{15}{2} = \frac{30}{6}$, and $\frac{30}{6} = 5$.

Notice that in the first example, the number of groups is greater than 1 (5 people) and in the second, the number of groups is less than 1 ($\frac{2}{3}$ of a pitcher), but the division and multiplication equations for both situations have the same structures.

iM KH

# Lesson 8 Practice Problems

1. For each situation, complete the tape diagram to represent and answer the question.

    a. Mai has picked 1 cup of strawberries for a cake, which is enough for $\frac{3}{4}$ of the cake. How many cups does she need for the whole cake?

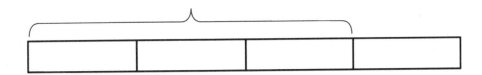

    b. Priya has picked $1\frac{1}{2}$ cups of raspberries, which is enough for $\frac{3}{4}$ of a cake. How many cups does she need for the whole cake?

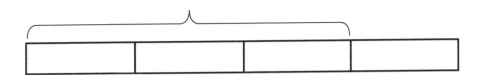

2. Consider the problem: Tyler painted $\frac{9}{2}$ square yards of wall area with 3 gallons of paint. How many gallons of paint does it take to paint each square yard of wall?

    a. Write multiplication and division equations to represent the situation.

    b. Draw a diagram to represent and answer the question.

3. Consider the problem: After walking $\frac{1}{4}$ mile from home, Han is $\frac{1}{3}$ of his way to school. What is the distance between his home and school?

   a. Write multiplication and division equations to represent this situation.

   b. Complete the diagram to represent and answer the question.

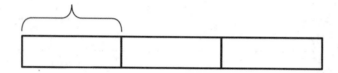

4. Here is a division equation: $\frac{4}{5} \div \frac{2}{3} = ?$

   a. Write a multiplication equation that corresponds to the division equation.

   b. Draw a diagram to represent and answer the question.

   (From Unit 4, Lesson 7.)

iM KH

5. Consider the problem: A set of books that are each 1.5 inches wide are being organized on a bookshelf that is 36 inches wide. How many books can fit on the shelf?

   a. Write multiplication and division equations to represent the situation.

   b. Find the answer. Draw a diagram, if needed.

   c. Use the multiplication equation to check your answer.

   (From Unit 4, Lesson 3.)

6.   a. Without calculating, order the quotients from smallest to largest.

   $56 \div 8$                    $56 \div 8,000,000$                $56 \div 0.000008$

   b. Explain how you decided the order of the three expressions.

   c. Find a number $n$ so that $56 \div n$ is greater than 1 but less than 7.

   (From Unit 4, Lesson 1.)

# Lesson 9: How Much in Each Group? (Part 2)

Let's practice dividing fractions in different situations.

## 9.1: Number Talk: Greater Than 1 or Less Than 1?

Decide whether each quotient is greater than 1 or less than 1.

$\frac{1}{2} \div \frac{1}{4}$  $\frac{2}{1} = 2$

$1 \div \frac{3}{4}$  $\frac{4}{3} = 1\frac{1}{3}$

$\frac{2}{3} \div \frac{7}{8}$  $\frac{16}{21} = \frac{16}{21}$

$2\frac{7}{8} \div 2\frac{3}{5}$

$\frac{23}{8} \times \frac{5}{13}$  $\frac{115}{104} = 1\frac{11}{104}$

## 9.2: Two Water Containers

1. After looking at these pictures, Lin says, "I see the fraction $\frac{2}{5}$." Jada says, "I see the fraction $\frac{3}{4}$." What quantities are Lin and Jada referring to?

2. Consider the problem: How many liters of water fit in the water dispenser?

    a. Write a multiplication equation and a division equation for the question.

    b. Find the answer and explain your reasoning. If you get stuck, consider drawing a diagram.

    c. Check your answer using the multiplication equation.

## 9.3: Amount in One Group

Write a multiplication equation and a division equation and draw a diagram to represent each situation. Then, find the answer and explain your reasoning.

1. Jada bought $3\frac{1}{2}$ yards of fabric for $21. How much did each yard cost?

$$\frac{3}{\phantom{x}} \times \frac{2}{1} = \frac{6}{1} = 6$$

2. $\frac{4}{9}$ kilogram of baking soda costs $2. How much does 1 kilogram of baking soda cost?

$$2 \div \frac{4}{9}$$

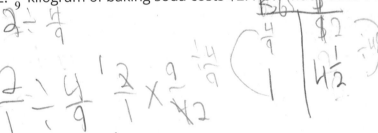

$$\frac{2}{1} \div \frac{4}{9} \quad \frac{2}{1} \times \frac{9}{4} = 2$$

3. Diego can fill $1\frac{1}{5}$ bottles with 3 liters of water. How many liters of water fill 1 bottle?

4. $\frac{5}{4}$ gallons of water fill $\frac{5}{6}$ of a bucket. How many gallons of water fill the entire bucket?

**Are you ready for more?**

The largest sandwich ever made weighed 5,440 pounds. If everyone on Earth shares the sandwich equally, how much would you get? What fraction of a regular sandwich does this represent?

## 9.4: Inventing Another Situation

1. Think of a situation with a question that can be represented by $\frac{1}{3} \div \frac{1}{4} = ?$. Describe the situation and the question.

2. Trade descriptions with a partner.

   ○ Review each other's description and discuss whether each question matches the equation.
   ○ Revise your description based on the feedback from your partner.

3. Find the answer to your question. Explain or show your reasoning. If you get stuck, consider drawing a diagram.

**Lesson 9 Summary**

Sometimes we have to think carefully about how to solve a problem that involves multiplication and division. Diagrams and equations can help us.

For example, $\frac{3}{4}$ of a pound of rice fills $\frac{2}{5}$ of a container. There are two whole amounts to keep track of here: 1 whole pound and 1 whole container. The equations we write and the diagram we draw depend on what question we are trying to answer.

- How many pounds fill 1 container?

$$\frac{2}{5} \cdot ? = \frac{3}{4}$$

$$\frac{3}{4} \div \frac{2}{5} = ?$$

If $\frac{2}{5}$ of a container is filled with $\frac{3}{4}$ pound, then $\frac{1}{5}$ of a container is filled with half of $\frac{3}{4}$, or $\frac{3}{8}$, pound. One whole container then has $5 \cdot \frac{3}{8}$ (or $\frac{15}{8}$) pounds.

- What fraction of a container does 1 pound fill?

$$\frac{3}{4} \cdot ? = \frac{2}{5}$$

$$\frac{2}{5} \div \frac{3}{4} = ?$$

If $\frac{3}{4}$ pound fills $\frac{2}{5}$ of a container, then $\frac{1}{4}$ pound fills a third of $\frac{2}{5}$, or $\frac{2}{15}$, of a container. One whole pound then fills $4 \cdot \frac{2}{15}$ (or $\frac{8}{15}$) of a container.

## Lesson 9 Practice Problems

1. A group of friends is sharing $2\frac{1}{2}$ pounds of berries.

   a. If each friend received $\frac{5}{4}$ of a pound of berries, how many friends are sharing the berries?

   b. If 5 friends are sharing the berries, how many pounds of berries does each friend receive?

2. $\frac{2}{5}$ kilogram of soil fills $\frac{1}{3}$ of a container. Can 1 kilogram of soil fit in the container? Explain or show your reasoning.

3. After raining for $\frac{3}{4}$ of an hour, a rain gauge is $\frac{2}{5}$ filled. If it continues to rain at that rate for 15 more minutes, what fraction of the rain gauge will be filled?

   a. To help answer this question, Diego wrote the equation $\frac{3}{4} \div \frac{2}{5} = ?$. Explain why this equation does *not* represent the situation.

   b. Write a multiplication equation and a division equation that do represent the situation.

iM KH

4. 3 tickets to the museum cost $12.75. At this rate, what is the cost of:

    a. 1 ticket?

    b. 5 tickets?

(From Unit 2, Lesson 8.)

5. Elena went 60 meters in 15 seconds. Noah went 50 meters in 10 seconds. Elena and Noah both moved at a constant speed.

    a. How far did Elena go in 1 second?

    b. How far did Noah go in 1 second?

    c. Who went faster? Explain or show your reasoning.

(From Unit 2, Lesson 9.)

6. The first row in the table shows a recipe for 1 batch of trail mix. Complete the table to show recipes for 2, 3, and 4 batches of the same type of trail mix.

| number of batches | cups of cereal | cups of almonds | cups of raisins |
|---|---|---|---|
| 1 | 2 | $\frac{1}{3}$ | $\frac{1}{4}$ |
| 2 | | | |
| 3 | | | |
| 4 | | | |

(From Unit 2, Lesson 11.)

# Lesson 10: Dividing by Unit and Non-Unit Fractions

Let's look for patterns when we divide by a fraction.

## 10.1: Dividing by a Whole Number

Work with a partner. One person solves the problems labeled "Partner A" and the other person solves those labeled "Partner B." Write an equation for each question. If you get stuck, consider drawing a diagram.

1. Partner A:

   How many 3s are in 12?

   Division equation:

   $12 \div 3 = 4$

   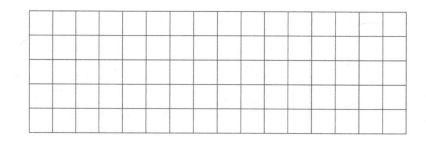

   How many 4s are in 12?

   Division equation:

   $12 \div 4 = 3$

   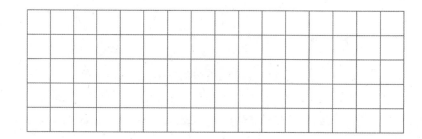

   How many 6s are in 12?

   Division equation:

   $12 \div 6 = 2$

   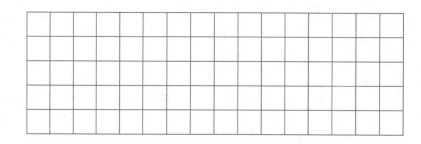

iM KH

Partner B:

What is 12 groups of $\frac{1}{3}$?

Multiplication equation:

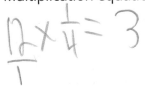

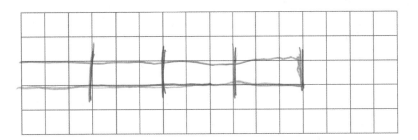

What is 12 groups of $\frac{1}{4}$?

Multiplication equation:

$$\frac{12}{1} \times \frac{1}{4} = 3$$

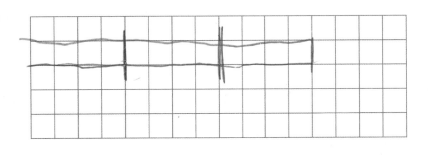

What is 12 groups of $\frac{1}{6}$?

Multiplication equation:

$$\frac{12}{1} \times \frac{1}{6} = 2$$

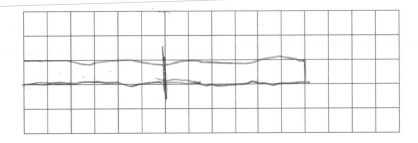

2. What do you notice about the diagrams and equations? Discuss with your partner.

3. Complete this sentence based on what you noticed:

   Dividing by a whole number $a$ produces the same result as multiplying by _____.

## 10.2: Dividing by Unit Fractions

To find the value of $6 \div \frac{1}{2}$, Elena thought, "How many $\frac{1}{2}$s are in 6?" and then she drew this tape diagram. It shows 6 ones, with each one partitioned into 2 equal pieces.

$6 \div \frac{1}{2}$

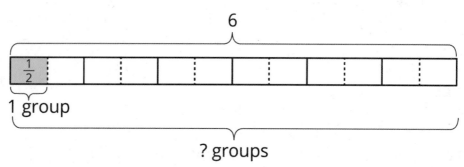

1. For each division expression, complete the diagram using the same method as Elena. Then, find the value of the expression.

   a.

   $6 \div \frac{1}{3}$

   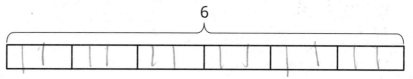

   Value of the expression: _____

   b.

   $6 \div \frac{1}{4}$

   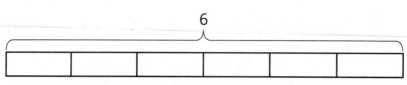

   Value of the expression: _____

   c.

   $6 \div \frac{1}{6}$

   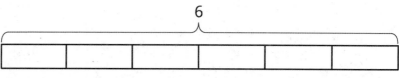

   Value of the expression: _____

2. Examine the expressions and answers more closely. Look for a pattern. How could you find how many halves, thirds, fourths, or sixths were in 6 without counting all of them? Explain your reasoning.

iM KH

3. Use the pattern you noticed to find the values of these expressions. If you get stuck, consider drawing a diagram.

a. $6 \div \frac{1}{8}$

b. $6 \div \frac{1}{10}$

c. $6 \div \frac{1}{25}$

d. $6 \div \frac{1}{b}$

4. Find the value of each expression.

a. $8 \div \frac{1}{4}$

b. $12 \div \frac{1}{5}$

c. $a \div \frac{1}{2}$

d. $a \div \frac{1}{b}$

## 10.3: Dividing by Non-unit Fractions

1. To find the value of $6 \div \frac{2}{3}$, Elena started by drawing a diagram the same way she did for $6 \div \frac{1}{3}$.

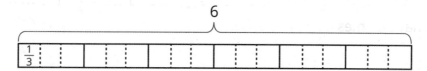

a. Complete the diagram to show how many $\frac{2}{3}$s are in 6.

b. Elena says, "To find $6 \div \frac{2}{3}$, I can just take the value of $6 \div \frac{1}{3}$ and then either multiply it by $\frac{1}{2}$ or divide it by 2." Do you agree with her? Explain your reasoning.

2. For each division expression, complete the diagram using the same method as Elena. Then, find the value of the expression. Think about how you could find that value without counting all the pieces in your diagram.

a.

$6 \div \frac{3}{4}$

6

Value of the expression:_____

b.

$6 \div \frac{4}{3}$

6

Value of the expression:_____

c.

$6 \div \frac{4}{6}$

6

Value of the expression:_____

iM KH

3. Elena examined her diagrams and noticed that she always took the same two steps to show division by a fraction on a tape diagram. She said:

"My first step was to divide each 1 whole into as many parts as the number in the denominator. So if the expression is $6 \div \frac{3}{4}$, I would break each 1 whole into 4 parts. Now I have 4 times as many parts.

My second step was to put a certain number of those parts into one group, and that number is the numerator of the divisor. So if the fraction is $\frac{3}{4}$, I would put 3 of the $\frac{1}{4}$s into one group. Then I could tell how many $\frac{3}{4}$s are in 6."

Which expression represents how many $\frac{3}{4}$s Elena would have after these two steps? Be prepared to explain your reasoning.

- $6 \div 4 \cdot 3$                          ○ $6 \cdot 4 \div 3$

- $6 \div 4 \div 3$                          ○ $6 \cdot 4 \cdot 3$

4. Use the pattern Elena noticed to find the values of these expressions. If you get stuck, consider drawing a diagram.

   a. $6 \div \frac{2}{7}$

   b. $6 \div \frac{3}{10}$

   c. $6 \div \frac{6}{25}$

## Are you ready for more?

Find the missing value.

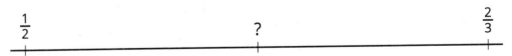

## Lesson 10 Summary

To answer the question "How many $\frac{1}{3}$s are in 4?" or "What is $4 \div \frac{1}{3}$?", we can reason that there are 3 thirds in 1, so there are $(4 \cdot 3)$ thirds in 4.

In other words, dividing 4 by $\frac{1}{3}$ has the same result as multiplying 4 by 3.

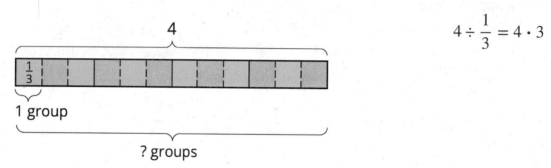

$$4 \div \frac{1}{3} = 4 \cdot 3$$

In general, dividing a number by a unit fraction $\frac{1}{b}$ is the same as multiplying the number by $b$, which is the **reciprocal** of $\frac{1}{b}$.

How can we reason about $4 \div \frac{2}{3}$?

We already know that there are $(4 \cdot 3)$ or 12 groups of $\frac{1}{3}$s in 4. To find how many $\frac{2}{3}$s are in 4, we need to put together every 2 of the $\frac{1}{3}$s into a group. Doing this results in half as many groups, which is 6 groups. In other words:

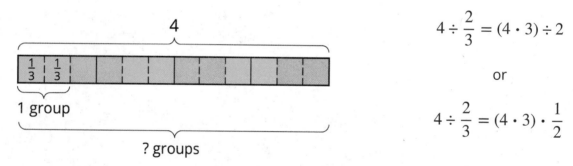

$$4 \div \frac{2}{3} = (4 \cdot 3) \div 2$$

or

$$4 \div \frac{2}{3} = (4 \cdot 3) \cdot \frac{1}{2}$$

In general, dividing a number by $\frac{a}{b}$, is the same as multiplying the number by $b$ and then dividing by $a$, or multiplying the number by $b$ and then by $\frac{1}{a}$.

## Glossary

- reciprocal

iM KH

# Lesson 10 Practice Problems

1. Priya is sharing 24 apples equally with some friends. She uses division to determine how many people can have a share if each person gets a particular number of apples. For example, $24 \div 4 = 6$ means that if each person gets 4 apples, then 6 people can have apples. Here are some other calculations:

   $24 \div 4 = 6$ $\qquad$ $24 \div 2 = 12$ $\qquad$ $24 \div 1 = 24$ $\qquad$ $24 \div \frac{1}{2} = ?$

   a. Priya thinks the "?" represents a number less than 24. Do you agree? Explain or show your reasoning.

   b. In the case of $24 \div \frac{1}{2} = ?$, how many people can have apples?

2. Here is a centimeter ruler.

   a. Use the ruler to find $1 \div \frac{1}{10}$ and $4 \div \frac{1}{10}$.

   b. What calculation did you do each time?

   c. Use this pattern to find $18 \div \frac{1}{10}$.

   d. Explain how you could find $4 \div \frac{2}{10}$ and $4 \div \frac{8}{10}$.

3. Find each quotient.

   a. $5 \div \frac{1}{10}$

   b. $5 \div \frac{3}{10}$

   c. $5 \div \frac{9}{10}$

4. Use the fact that $2\frac{1}{2} \div \frac{1}{8} = 20$ to find $2\frac{1}{2} \div \frac{5}{8}$. Explain or show your reasoning.

5. Consider the problem: It takes one week for a crew of workers to pave $\frac{3}{5}$ kilometer of a road. At that rate, how long will it take to pave 1 kilometer?

    Write a multiplication equation and a division equation to represent the question. Then find the answer and show your reasoning.

    (From Unit 4, Lesson 9.)

6. A box contains $1\frac{3}{4}$ pounds of pancake mix. Jada used $\frac{7}{8}$ pound for a recipe. What fraction of the pancake mix in the box did she use? Explain or show your reasoning. Draw a diagram, if needed.

    (From Unit 4, Lesson 7.)

7. Calculate each percentage mentally.

    a. 25% of 400        a. 75% of 200        a. 5% of 20

    b. 50% of 90         b. 10% of 8,000

    (From Unit 3, Lesson 14.)

iM KH

# Lesson 11: Using an Algorithm to Divide Fractions

Let's divide fractions using the rule we learned.

## 11.1: Multiplying Fractions

Evaluate each expression.

1. $\frac{2}{3} \cdot 27$

2. $\frac{1}{2} \cdot \frac{2}{3}$

3. $\frac{2}{9} \cdot \frac{3}{5}$

4. $\frac{27}{100} \cdot \frac{200}{9}$

5. $\left(1\frac{3}{4}\right) \cdot \frac{5}{7}$

## 11.2: Dividing a Fraction by a Fraction

Work with a partner. One person works on the questions labeled "Partner A" and the other person works on those labeled "Partner B."

1. Partner A: Find the value of each expression by completing the diagram.

a.

$\frac{3}{4} \div \frac{1}{8}$

How many $\frac{1}{8}$s in $\frac{3}{4}$?

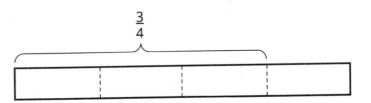

b.

$\frac{9}{10} \div \frac{3}{5}$

How many $\frac{3}{5}$s in $\frac{9}{10}$?

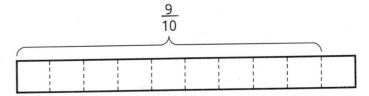

Partner B:

Elena said, "If I want to divide 4 by $\frac{2}{5}$, I can multiply 4 by 5 and then divide it by 2 or multiply it by $\frac{1}{2}$."

Find the value of each expression using the strategy Elena described.

a. $\frac{3}{4} \div \frac{1}{8}$

b. $\frac{9}{10} \div \frac{3}{5}$

2. What do you notice about the diagrams and expressions? Discuss with your partner.

3. Complete this sentence based on what you noticed:

To divide a number $n$ by a fraction $\frac{a}{b}$, we can multiply $n$ by _____ and then divide the product by _____.

4. Select **all** the equations that represent the sentence you completed.

○ $n \div \frac{a}{b} = n \cdot b \div a$

○ $n \div \frac{a}{b} = n \cdot a \div b$

○ $n \div \frac{a}{b} = n \cdot \frac{a}{b}$

○ $n \div \frac{a}{b} = n \cdot \frac{b}{a}$

iM KH

## 11.3: Using an Algorithm to Divide Fractions

Calculate each quotient. Show your thinking and be prepared to explain your reasoning.

1. $\frac{8}{9} \div 4$     $\frac{\overset{2}{\cancel{8}}}{9} \times \frac{1}{\cancel{4}1} \qquad \frac{2}{9}$

2. $\frac{3}{4} \div \frac{1}{2}$     $\frac{3}{2\cancel{4}} \times \frac{\cancel{2}1}{1} = \frac{3}{2}$ or $1\frac{1}{2}$

3. $3\frac{1}{3} \div \frac{2}{9}$     $\frac{5\overset{\cancel{10}}{\cancel{3}}}{1\cancel{3}} \times \frac{\overset{3}{\cancel{9}}}{\cancel{2}2} = \frac{15}{1}$ or $15$

4. $\frac{9}{2} \div \frac{3}{8}$     $\frac{\overset{3}{\cancel{9}}}{1\cancel{2}} \times \frac{\overset{4}{\cancel{8}}}{\cancel{3}1} = \frac{12}{1}$ or $12$

5. $6\frac{2}{5} \div 3$     $\frac{32}{5} \times \frac{1}{3} = \frac{32}{15}$ or $2\frac{2}{15}$

6. After biking $5\frac{1}{2}$ miles, Jada has traveled $\frac{2}{3}$ of the length of her trip. How long (in miles) is the entire length of her trip? Write an equation to represent the situation, and then find the answer.

$\frac{11}{2} \times \frac{3}{2} = \frac{33}{4}$

$\frac{33}{4}$ or $8\frac{1}{4}$

## Are you ready for more?

Suppose you have a pint of grape juice and a pint of milk. You pour 1 tablespoon of the grape juice into the milk and mix it up. Then you pour 1 tablespoon of this mixture back into the grape juice. Which liquid is more contaminated?

## Lesson 11 Summary

The division $a \div \frac{3}{4} = ?$ is equivalent to $\frac{3}{4} \cdot ? = a$, so we can think of it as meaning "$\frac{3}{4}$ of what number is $a$?" and represent it with a diagram as shown. The length of the entire diagram represents the unknown number.

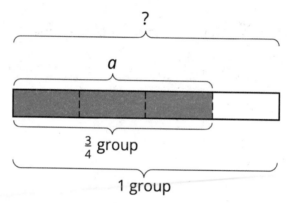

If $\frac{3}{4}$ of a number is $a$, then to find the number, we can first divide $a$ by 3 to find $\frac{1}{4}$ of the number. Then we multiply the result by 4 to find the number.

The steps above can be written as: $a \div 3 \cdot 4$. Dividing by 3 is the same as multiplying by $\frac{1}{3}$, so we can also write the steps as: $a \cdot \frac{1}{3} \cdot 4$.

In other words: $a \div 3 \cdot 4 = a \cdot \frac{1}{3} \cdot 4$. And $a \cdot \frac{1}{3} \cdot 4 = a \cdot \frac{4}{3}$, so we can say that:

$$a \div \frac{3}{4} = a \cdot \frac{4}{3}$$

In general, dividing a number by a fraction $\frac{c}{d}$ is the same as multiplying the number by $\frac{d}{c}$, which is the reciprocal of the fraction.

iM KH

# Lesson 11 Practice Problems

1. Select **all** the statements that show correct reasoning for finding $\frac{14}{15} \div \frac{7}{5}$.

   A. Multiplying $\frac{14}{15}$ by 5 and then by $\frac{1}{7}$.

   B. Dividing $\frac{14}{15}$ by 5, and then multiplying by $\frac{1}{7}$.

   C. Multiplying $\frac{14}{15}$ by 7, and then multiplying by $\frac{1}{5}$.

   D. Multiplying $\frac{14}{15}$ by 5 and then dividing by 7.

   E. Multiplying $\frac{15}{14}$ by 7 and then dividing by 5.

2. Clare said that $\frac{4}{3} \div \frac{5}{2}$ is $\frac{10}{3}$. She reasoned: $\frac{4}{3} \cdot 5 = \frac{20}{3}$ and $\frac{20}{3} \div 2 = \frac{10}{3}$.

   Explain why Clare's answer and reasoning are incorrect. Find the correct quotient.

3. Find the value of $\frac{15}{4} \div \frac{5}{8}$. Show your reasoning.

4. Consider the problem: Kiran has $2\frac{3}{4}$ pounds of flour. When he divides the flour into equal-sized bags, he fills $4\frac{1}{8}$ bags. How many pounds fit in each bag?

   Write a multiplication equation and a division equation to represent the question. Then, find the answer and show your reasoning.

5. Divide $4\frac{1}{2}$ by each of these unit fractions.

    a. $\frac{1}{8}$

    b. $\frac{1}{4}$

    c. $\frac{1}{6}$

(From Unit 4, Lesson 10.)

6. Consider the problem: After charging for $\frac{1}{3}$ of an hour, a phone is at $\frac{2}{5}$ of its full power. How long will it take the phone to charge completely?

Decide whether each equation can represent the situation.

    a. $\frac{1}{3} \cdot ? = \frac{2}{5}$

    b. $\frac{1}{3} \div \frac{2}{5} = ?$

    c. $\frac{2}{5} \div \frac{1}{3} = ?$

    d. $\frac{2}{5} \cdot ? = \frac{1}{3}$

(From Unit 4, Lesson 9.)

7. Elena and Noah are each filling a bucket with water. Noah's bucket is $\frac{2}{5}$ full and the water weighs $2\frac{1}{2}$ pounds. How much does Elena's water weigh if her bucket is full and her bucket is identical to Noah's?

    a. Write multiplication and division equations to represent the question.

    b. Draw a diagram to show the relationship between the quantities and to find the answer.

(From Unit 4, Lesson 8.)

iM KH

# Lesson 12: Fractional Lengths

Let's solve problems about fractional lengths.

## 12.1: Number Talk: Multiplication Strategies

Find the product mentally.

$19 \cdot 14$

## 12.2: Info Gap: How Many Would It Take?

Your teacher will give you either a *problem card* or a *data card*. Do not show or read your card to your partner.

If your teacher gives you the *problem card*:

1. Silently read your card and think about what information you need to be able to answer the question.

2. Ask your partner for the specific information that you need.

3. Explain how you are using the information to solve the problem.

    Continue to ask questions until you have enough information to solve the problem.

4. Share the *problem card* and solve the problem independently.

5. Read the *data card* and discuss your reasoning.

If your teacher gives you the *data card*:

1. Silently read your card.

2. Ask your partner *"What specific information do you need?"* and wait for them to *ask* for information.

    If your partner asks for information that is not on the card, do not do the calculations for them. Tell them you don't have that information.

3. Before sharing the information, ask *"Why do you need that information?"* Listen to your partner's reasoning and ask clarifying questions.

4. Read the *problem card* and solve the problem independently.

5. Share the *data card* and discuss your reasoning.

**Are you ready for more?**

Lin has a work of art that is 14 inches by 20 inches. She wants to frame it with large paper clips laid end to end.

1. If each paper clip is $1\frac{3}{4}$ inch long, how many paper clips would she need? Show your reasoning and be sure to think about potential gaps and overlaps. Consider making a sketch that shows how the paper clips could be arranged.

2. How many paper clips are needed if the paper clips are spaced $\frac{1}{4}$ inch apart? Describe the arrangement of the paper clips at the corners of the frame.

## 12.3: How Many Times as Tall or as Far?

1. A second-grade student is 4 feet tall. Her teacher is $5\frac{2}{3}$ feet tall.

   a. How many times as tall as the student is the teacher?

   $\frac{17}{5} \times \frac{1}{4}$   $\frac{17}{12}$   $1\frac{5}{12}$

   b. What fraction of the teacher's height is the student's height?

   $\frac{4}{1} \times \frac{3}{17}$   $\frac{12}{17}$

2. Find each quotient. Show your reasoning and check your answer.

   a. $9 \div \frac{3}{5}$   $\frac{3}{1}\frac{9}{1} \times \frac{5}{3}$   $\frac{15}{1}$

   b. $1\frac{7}{8} \div \frac{3}{4}$   $\frac{5}{2}\frac{15}{8} \times \frac{4}{3}$   $\frac{5}{2}$   $2\frac{1}{2}$

3. Write a division equation that can help answer each of these questions. Then find the answer. If you get stuck, consider drawing a diagram.

a. A runner ran $1\frac{4}{5}$ miles on Monday and $6\frac{3}{10}$ miles on Tuesday. How many times her Monday's distance was her Tuesday's distance?

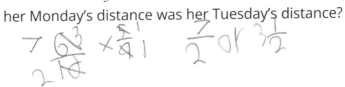

b. A cyclist planned to ride $9\frac{1}{2}$ miles but only managed to travel $3\frac{7}{8}$ miles. What fraction of his planned trip did he travel?

## 12.4: Comparing Paper Rolls

The photo shows a situation that involves fractions.

1. Complete the sentences. Be prepared to explain your reasoning.

a. The length of the long tube is about _____ times the length of a short tube.

b. The length of a short tube is about _____ times the length of the long tube.

2. If the length of the long paper roll is $11\frac{1}{4}$ inches, what is the length of each short paper roll?

## Lesson 12 Summary

Division can help us solve comparison problems in which we find out how many times as large or as small one number is compared to another. For example, a student is playing two songs for a music recital. The first song is $1\frac{1}{2}$ minutes long. The second song is $3\frac{3}{4}$ minutes long.

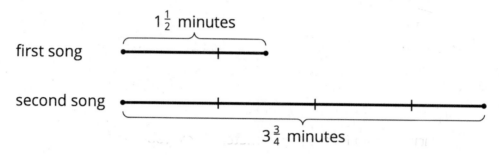

We can ask two different comparison questions and write different multiplication and division equations to represent each question.

- How many times as long as the first song is the second song?

$$? \cdot 1\frac{1}{2} = 3\frac{3}{4}$$

$$3\frac{3}{4} \div 1\frac{1}{2} = ?$$

- What fraction of the second song is the first song?

$$? \cdot 3\frac{3}{4} = 1\frac{1}{2}$$

$$1\frac{1}{2} \div 3\frac{3}{4} = ?$$

We can use the algorithm we learned to calculate the quotients.

$$= \frac{15}{4} \div \frac{3}{2}$$

$$= \frac{15}{4} \cdot \frac{2}{3}$$

$$= \frac{30}{12}$$

$$= \frac{5}{2}$$

$$= \frac{3}{2} \div \frac{15}{4}$$

$$= \frac{3}{2} \cdot \frac{4}{15}$$

$$= \frac{12}{30}$$

$$= \frac{2}{5}$$

This means the second song is $2\frac{1}{2}$ times as long as the first song.

This means the first song is $\frac{2}{5}$ as long as the second song.

iM KH

# Lesson 12 Practice Problems

1. One inch is around $2\frac{11}{20}$ centimeters.

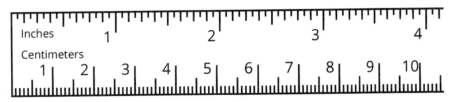

   a. How many centimeters long is 3 inches? Show your reasoning.

   b. What fraction of an inch is 1 centimeter? Show your reasoning.

   c. What question can be answered by finding $10 \div 2\frac{11}{20}$ in this situation?

2. A zookeeper is $6\frac{1}{4}$ feet tall. A young giraffe in his care is $9\frac{3}{8}$ feet tall.

   a. How many times as tall as the zookeeper is the giraffe?

   b. What fraction of the giraffe's height is the zookeeper's height?

3. A rectangular bathroom floor is covered with square tiles that are $1\frac{1}{2}$ feet by $1\frac{1}{2}$ feet. The length of the bathroom floor is $10\frac{1}{2}$ feet and the width is $6\frac{1}{2}$ feet.

   a. How many tiles does it take to cover the length of the floor?

   b. How many tiles does it take to cover the width of the floor?

4. The Food and Drug Administration (FDA) recommends a certain amount of nutrient intake per day called the "daily value." Food labels usually show percentages of the daily values for several different nutrients—calcium, iron, vitamins, etc.

Consider the problem: In $\frac{3}{4}$ cup of oatmeal, there is $\frac{1}{10}$ of the recommended daily value of iron. What fraction of the daily recommended value of iron is in 1 cup of oatmeal?

Write a multiplication equation and a division equation to represent the question. Then find the answer and show your reasoning.

(From Unit 4, Lesson 11.)

5. What fraction of $\frac{1}{2}$ is $\frac{1}{3}$? Draw a tape diagram to represent and answer the question. Use graph paper if needed.

(From Unit 4, Lesson 7.)

6. Noah says, "There are $2\frac{1}{2}$ groups of $\frac{4}{5}$ in 2." Do you agree with him? Draw a tape diagram to show your reasoning. Use graph paper, if needed.

(From Unit 4, Lesson 6.)

iM KH

# Lesson 13: Rectangles with Fractional Side Lengths

Let's explore rectangles that have fractional measurements.

## 13.1: Areas of Squares

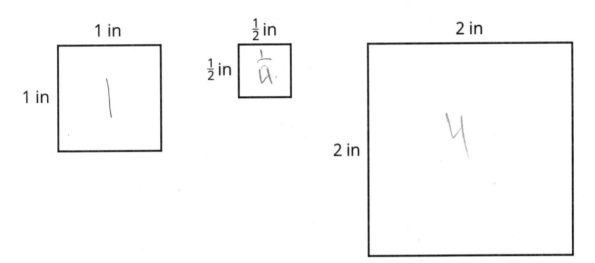

1. What do you notice about the areas of the squares?

2. Kiran says "A square with side lengths of $\frac{1}{3}$ inch has an area of $\frac{1}{3}$ square inches." Do you agree? Explain or show your reasoning.

# 13.2: Areas of Squares and Rectangles

Your teacher will give you graph paper and a ruler.

1. On the graph paper, draw a square with side lengths of 1 inch. Inside this square, draw another square with side lengths of $\frac{1}{4}$ inch.

   Use your drawing to answer the questions.

   a. How many squares with side lengths of $\frac{1}{4}$ inch can fit in a square with side lengths of 1 inch?

   b. What is the area of a square with side lengths of $\frac{1}{4}$ inch? Explain or show your reasoning.

2. On the graph paper, draw a rectangle that is $3\frac{1}{2}$ inches by $2\frac{1}{4}$ inches.

   For each question, write a division expression and then find the answer.

   a. How many $\frac{1}{4}$-inch segments are in a length of $3\frac{1}{2}$ inches?

   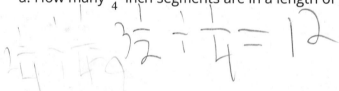

   $3\frac{1}{2} \div \frac{1}{4} = 12$

   b. How many $\frac{1}{4}$-inch segments are in a length of $2\frac{1}{4}$ inches?

   $2\frac{1}{4} \div \frac{1}{4} = 9$

3. Use your drawing to show that a rectangle that is $3\frac{1}{2}$ inches by $2\frac{1}{4}$ inches has an area of $7\frac{7}{8}$ square inches.

   $\frac{7}{2} \times \frac{9}{4} = \frac{63}{8}$ or $7\frac{7}{8}$

## 13.3: Areas of Rectangles

Each of these multiplication expressions represents the area of a rectangle.

$2 \cdot 4$  $\qquad$ $2\frac{1}{2} \cdot 4$ $\qquad$ $2 \cdot 4\frac{3}{4}$ $\qquad$ $2\frac{1}{2} \cdot 4\frac{3}{4}$

1. All regions shaded in light blue have the same area. Match each diagram to the expression that you think represents its area. Be prepared to explain your reasoning.

A  B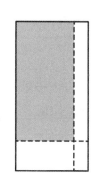

C  D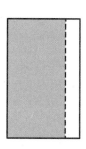

2. Use the diagram that matches $2\frac{1}{2} \cdot 4\frac{3}{4}$ to show that the value of $2\frac{1}{2} \cdot 4\frac{3}{4}$ is $11\frac{7}{8}$.

## Are you ready for more?

The following rectangles are composed of squares, and each rectangle is constructed using the previous rectangle. The side length of the first square is 1 unit.

1. Draw the next four rectangles that are constructed in the same way. Then complete the table with the side lengths of the rectangle and the fraction of the longer side over the shorter side.

| short side | long side | $\frac{\text{long side}}{\text{short side}}$ |
|---|---|---|
| 1 | | |
| 1 | | |
| 2 | | |
| 3 | | |
| | | |
| | | |
| | | |
| | | |
| | | |

2. Describe the values of the fraction of the longer side over the shorter side. What happens to the fraction as the pattern continues?

iM KH

## 13.4: How Many Would it Take? (Part 2)

Noah would like to cover a rectangular tray with rectangular tiles. The tray has a width of $11\frac{1}{4}$ inches and an area of $50\frac{5}{8}$ square inches.

1. Find the length of the tray in inches.

2. If the tiles are $\frac{3}{4}$ inch by $\frac{9}{16}$ inch, how many would Noah need to cover the tray completely, without gaps or overlaps? Explain or show your reasoning.

3. Draw a diagram to show how Noah could lay the tiles. Your diagram should show how many tiles would be needed to cover the length and width of the tray, but does not need to show every tile.

## Lesson 13 Summary

If a rectangle has side lengths $a$ units and $b$ units, the area is $a \cdot b$ square units. For example, if we have a rectangle with $\frac{1}{2}$-inch side lengths, its area is $\frac{1}{2} \cdot \frac{1}{2}$ or $\frac{1}{4}$ square inches.

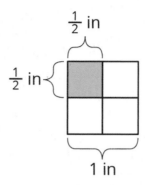

This means that if we know the *area* and *one side length* of a rectangle, we can divide to find the *other* side length.

$10\frac{1}{2}$ in

?      $89\frac{1}{4}$ in$^2$

If one side length of a rectangle is $10\frac{1}{2}$ in and its area is $89\frac{1}{4}$ in$^2$, we can write this equation to show their relationship:

$$10\frac{1}{2} \cdot \; ? = 89\frac{1}{4}$$

Then, we can find the other side length, in inches, using division:

$$89\frac{1}{4} \div 10\frac{1}{2} = \; ?$$

iM KH

# Lesson 13 Practice Problems

1.   a. Find the unknown side length of the rectangle if its area is 11 m². Show your reasoning.

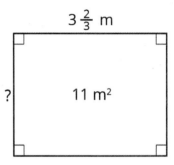

$3\frac{2}{3}$ m

? | 11 m²

   b. Check your answer by multiplying it by the given side length ($3\frac{2}{3}$). Is the resulting product 11? If not, revise your previous work.

2. A worker is tiling the floor of a rectangular room that is 12 feet by 15 feet. The tiles are square with side lengths $1\frac{1}{3}$ feet. How many tiles are needed to cover the entire floor? Show your reasoning.

3. A television screen has length $16\frac{1}{2}$ inches, width $w$ inches, and area 462 square inches. Select **all** the equations that represent the relationship of the side lengths and area of the television.

   A. $w \cdot 462 = 16\frac{1}{2}$

   B. $16\frac{1}{2} \cdot w = 462$

   C. $462 \div 16\frac{1}{2} = w$

   D. $462 \div w = 16\frac{1}{2}$

   E. $16\frac{1}{2} \cdot 462 = w$

4. The area of a rectangle is $17\frac{1}{2}$ in$^2$ and its shorter side is $3\frac{1}{2}$ in. Draw a diagram that shows this information. What is the length of the longer side?

5. A bookshelf is 42 inches long.

   a. How many books of length $1\frac{1}{2}$ inches will fit on the bookshelf? Explain your reasoning.

   b. A bookcase has 5 of these bookshelves. How many feet of shelf space is there? Explain your reasoning.

(From Unit 4, Lesson 12.)

6. Find the value of $\frac{5}{32} \div \frac{25}{4}$. Show your reasoning.

(From Unit 4, Lesson 11.)

iM KH

7. How many groups of $1\frac{2}{3}$ are in each of these quantities?

   a. $1\frac{5}{6}$

   b. $4\frac{1}{3}$

   c. $\frac{5}{6}$

   (From Unit 4, Lesson 6.)

8. It takes $1\frac{1}{4}$ minutes to fill a 3-gallon bucket of water with a hose. At this rate, how long does it take to fill a 50-gallon tub? If you get stuck, consider using a table.

   (From Unit 2, Lesson 14.)

# Lesson 14: Fractional Lengths in Triangles and Prisms

Let's explore area and volume when fractions are involved.

## 14.1: Area of Triangle

Find the area of Triangle A in square centimeters. Show your reasoning.

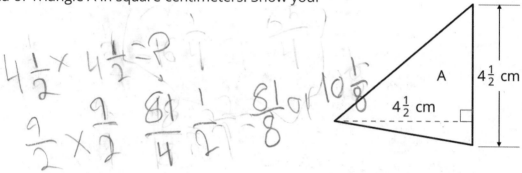

## 14.2: Bases and Heights of Triangles

1. The area of Triangle B is 8 square units. Find the length of $b$. Show your reasoning.

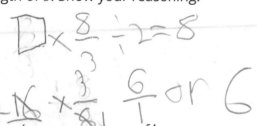

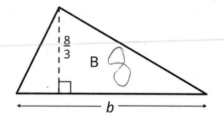

2. The area of Triangle C is $\frac{54}{5}$ square units. What is the length of $h$? Show your reasoning.

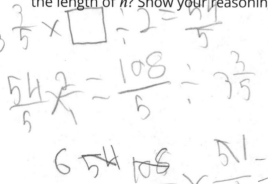

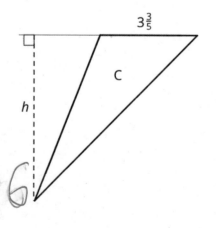

iM KH

# 14.3: Volumes of Cubes and Prisms

Your teacher will give you cubes that have edge lengths of $\frac{1}{2}$ inch.

1. Here is a drawing of a cube with edge lengths of 1 inch.

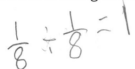

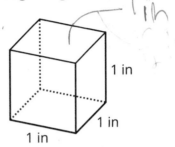

1 in

1 in

1 in

a. How many cubes with edge lengths of $\frac{1}{2}$ inch are needed to fill this cube?

b. What is the volume, in cubic inches, of a cube with edge lengths of $\frac{1}{2}$ inch? Explain or show your reasoning.

2. Four cubes are piled in a single stack to make a prism. Each cube has an edge length of $\frac{1}{2}$ inch. Sketch the prism, and find its volume in cubic inches.

3. Use cubes with an edge length of $\frac{1}{2}$ inch to build prisms with the lengths, widths, and heights shown in the table.

a. For each prism, record in the table how many $\frac{1}{2}$-inch cubes can be packed into the prism and the volume of the prism.

| prism length (in) | prism width (in) | prism height (in) | number of $\frac{1}{2}$-inch cubes in prism | volume of prism (in$^3$) |
|---|---|---|---|---|
| $\frac{1}{2}$ | $\frac{1}{2}$ | $\frac{1}{2}$ | | |
| 1 | 1 | $\frac{1}{2}$ | | |
| 2 | 1 | $\frac{1}{2}$ | | |
| 2 | 2 | 1 | | |
| 4 | 2 | $\frac{3}{2}$ | | |
| 5 | 4 | 2 | | |
| 5 | 4 | $2\frac{1}{2}$ | | |

b. Examine the values in the table. What do you notice about the relationship between the edge lengths of each prism and its volume?

4. What is the volume of a rectangular prism that is $1\frac{1}{2}$ inches by $2\frac{1}{4}$ inches by 4 inches? Show your reasoning.

**Are you ready for more?**

A unit fraction has a 1 in the numerator.

- These are unit fractions: $\frac{1}{3}, \frac{1}{100}, \frac{1}{1}$.
- These are *not* unit fractions: $\frac{2}{9}, \frac{8}{1}, 2\frac{1}{5}$.

1. Find three unit fractions whose sum is $\frac{1}{2}$. An example is: $\frac{1}{8} + \frac{1}{8} + \frac{1}{4} = \frac{1}{2}$ How many examples like this can you find?

2. Find a box whose surface area in square units equals its volume in cubic units. How many like this can you find?

## Lesson 14 Summary

If a rectangular prism has edge lengths of 2 units, 3 units, and 5 units, we can think of it as 2 layers of unit cubes, with each layer having $(3 \cdot 5)$ unit cubes in it. So the volume, in cubic units, is:

$$2 \cdot 3 \cdot 5$$

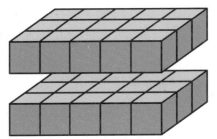

To find the volume of a rectangular prism with fractional edge lengths, we can think of it as being built of cubes that have a unit fraction for their edge length. For instance, if we build a prism that is $\frac{1}{2}$-inch tall, $\frac{3}{2}$-inch wide, and 4 inches long using cubes with a $\frac{1}{2}$-inch edge length, we would have:

- A height of 1 cube, because $1 \cdot \frac{1}{2} = \frac{1}{2}$.
- A width of 3 cubes, because $3 \cdot \frac{1}{2} = \frac{3}{2}$.
- A length of 8 cubes, because $8 \cdot \frac{1}{2} = 4$.

The volume of the prism would be $1 \cdot 3 \cdot 8$, or 24 cubic units. How do we find its volume in cubic inches? We know that each cube with a $\frac{1}{2}$-inch edge length has a volume of $\frac{1}{8}$ cubic inch, because $\frac{1}{2} \cdot \frac{1}{2} \cdot \frac{1}{2} = \frac{1}{8}$. Since the prism is built using 24 of these cubes, its volume, in cubic inches, would then be $24 \cdot \frac{1}{8}$, or 3 cubic inches.

The volume of the prism, in cubic inches, can also be found by multiplying the fractional edge lengths in inches: $\frac{1}{2} \cdot \frac{3}{2} \cdot 4 = 3$

# Lesson 14 Practice Problems

1. Clare is using little wooden cubes with edge length $\frac{1}{2}$ inch to build a larger cube that has edge length 4 inches. How many little cubes does she need? Explain your reasoning.

2. The triangle has an area of $7\frac{7}{8}$ cm$^2$ and a base of $5\frac{1}{4}$ cm.

   What is the length of $h$? Explain your reasoning.

   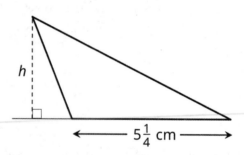

   $5\frac{1}{4}$ cm

3.     a. Which expression can be used to find how many cubes with edge length of $\frac{1}{3}$ unit fit in a prism that is 5 units by 5 units by 8 units? Explain or show your reasoning.

   ▪ $(5 \cdot \frac{1}{3}) \cdot (5 \cdot \frac{1}{3}) \cdot (8 \cdot \frac{1}{3})$

   ▪ $5 \cdot 5 \cdot 8$

   ▪ $(5 \cdot 3) \cdot (5 \cdot 3) \cdot (8 \cdot 3)$

   ▪ $(5 \cdot 5 \cdot 8) \cdot (\frac{1}{3})$

   b. Mai says that we can also find the answer by multiplying the edge lengths of the prism and then multiplying the result by 27. Do you agree with her? Explain your reasoning.

iM KH

4. A builder is building a fence with $6\frac{1}{4}$-inch-wide wooden boards, arranged side-by-side with no gaps or overlaps. How many boards are needed to build a fence that is 150 inches long? Show your reasoning.

(From Unit 4, Lesson 12.)

5. Find the value of each expression. Show your reasoning and check your answer.

   a. $2\frac{1}{7} \div \frac{2}{7}$

   b. $\frac{17}{20} \div \frac{1}{4}$

(From Unit 4, Lesson 12.)

6. Consider the problem: A bucket contains $11\frac{2}{3}$ gallons of water and is $\frac{5}{6}$ full. How many gallons of water would be in a full bucket?

   Write a multiplication and a division equation to represent the situation. Then, find the answer and show your reasoning.

(From Unit 4, Lesson 11.)

7. There are 80 kids in a gym. 75% are wearing socks. How many are *not* wearing socks? If you get stuck, consider using a tape diagram.

(From Unit 3, Lesson 12.)

8.    a. Lin wants to save $75 for a trip to the city. If she has saved $37.50 so far, what percentage of her goal has she saved? What percentage remains?

       b. Noah wants to save $60 so that he can purchase a concert ticket. If he has saved $45 so far, what percentage of his goal has he saved? What percentage remains?

(From Unit 3, Lesson 11.)

iM KH

# Lesson 15: Volume of Prisms

Let's look at the volume of prisms that have fractional measurements.

## 15.1: A Box of Cubes

1. How many cubes with an edge length of 1 inch fill this box?

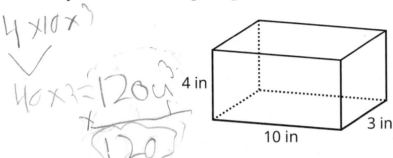

$4 \times 10 \times$

$40 \times 3 = 120$

$120$

2. If the cubes had an edge length of 2 inches, would you need more or fewer cubes to fill the box? Explain your reasoning.

15

$8 \overline{)120}$

$\underline{120}$

$0$

3. If the cubes had an edge length of $\frac{1}{2}$ inch, would you need more or fewer cubes to fill the box? Explain your reasoning.

$\frac{1}{2} \times \frac{1}{2} = \frac{1}{4} \times \frac{1}{2} = \frac{1}{8}$

$\frac{120}{1} \times \frac{8}{8} = \frac{960}{1}$ or 960

# 15.2: Cubes with Fractional Edge Lengths

1. Diego says that 108 cubes with an edge length of $\frac{1}{3}$ inch are needed to fill a rectangular prism that is 3 inches by 1 inch by $1\frac{1}{3}$ inch.

   a. Explain or show how this is true. If you get stuck, consider drawing a diagram.

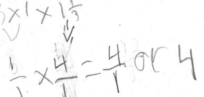

   b. What is the volume, in cubic inches, of the rectangular prism? Explain or show your reasoning.

2. Lin and Noah are packing small cubes into a larger cube with an edge length of $1\frac{1}{2}$ inches. Lin is using cubes with an edge length of $\frac{1}{2}$ inch, and Noah is using cubes with an edge length of $\frac{1}{4}$ inch.

   a. Who would need more cubes to fill the $1\frac{1}{2}$-inch cube? Be prepared to explain your reasoning.

   b. If Lin and Noah each use their small cubes to find the volume of the larger $1\frac{1}{2}$-inch cube, will they get the same answer? Explain or show your reasoning.

iM KH

## 15.3: Fish Tank and Baking Pan

1. A nature center has a fish tank in the shape of a rectangular prism. The tank is 10 feet long, $8\frac{1}{4}$ feet wide, and 6 feet tall.

    a. What is the volume of the tank in cubic feet? Explain or show your reasoning.

    b. The nature center's caretaker filled $\frac{4}{5}$ of the tank with water. What was the volume of the water in the tank, in cubic feet? What was the height of the water in the tank? Explain or show your reasoning.

    c. Another day, the tank was filled with 330 cubic feet of water. The height of the water was what fraction of the height of the tank? Show your reasoning.

2. Clare's recipe for banana bread won't fit in her favorite pan. The pan is $8\frac{1}{2}$ inches by 11 inches by 2 inches. The batter fills the pan to the very top, and when baking, the batter spills over the sides. To avoid spills, there should be about an inch between the top of the batter and the rim of the pan.

    Clare has another pan that is 9 inches by 9 inches by $2\frac{1}{2}$ inches. If she uses this pan, will the batter spill over during baking?

**Are you ready for more?**

1. Find the area of a rectangle with side lengths $\frac{1}{2}$ and $\frac{2}{3}$.

2. Find the volume of a rectangular prism with side lengths $\frac{1}{2}$, $\frac{2}{3}$, and $\frac{3}{4}$.

3. What do you think happens if we keep multiplying fractions $\frac{1}{2} \cdot \frac{2}{3} \cdot \frac{3}{4} \cdot \frac{4}{5} \cdot \frac{5}{6} \ldots$?

4. Find the area of a rectangle with side lengths $\frac{1}{1}$ and $\frac{2}{1}$.

5. Find the volume of a rectangular prism with side lengths $\frac{1}{1}$, $\frac{2}{1}$, and $\frac{1}{3}$.

6. What do you think happens if we keep multiplying fractions $\frac{1}{1} \cdot \frac{2}{1} \cdot \frac{1}{3} \cdot \frac{4}{1} \cdot \frac{1}{5} \ldots$?

## Lesson 15 Summary

If a rectangular prism has edge lengths $a$ units, $b$ units, and $c$ units, the volume is the product of $a$, $b$, and $c$.

$$V = a \cdot b \cdot c$$

This means that if we know the *volume* and *two edge lengths*, we can divide to find the *third* edge length.

Suppose the volume of a rectangular prism is $400\frac{1}{2}$ cm$^3$, one edge length is $\frac{11}{2}$ cm, another is 6 cm, and the third edge length is unknown. We can write a multiplication equation to represent the situation:

$$\frac{11}{2} \cdot 6 \cdot ? = 400\frac{1}{2}$$

We can find the third edge length by dividing:

$$400\frac{1}{2} \div \left( \frac{11}{2} \cdot 6 \right) = ?$$

iM KH

# Lesson 15 Practice Problems

1. A pool in the shape of a rectangular prism is being filled with water. The length and width of the pool is 24 feet and 15 feet. If the height of the water in the pool is $1\frac{1}{3}$ feet, what is the volume of the water in cubic feet?

2. A rectangular prism measures $2\frac{2}{5}$ inches by $3\frac{1}{5}$ inches by 2 inch.

   a. Priya said, "It takes more cubes with edge length $\frac{2}{5}$ inch than cubes with edge length $\frac{1}{5}$ inch to pack the prism." Do you agree with Priya? Explain or show your reasoning.

   b. How many cubes with edge length $\frac{1}{5}$ inch fit in the prism? Show your reasoning.

   c. Explain how you can use your answer in the previous question to find the volume of the prism in cubic inches.

3.    a. Here is a right triangle. What is its area?

   b. What is the height $h$ for the base that is $\frac{5}{4}$ units long? Show your reasoning.

   (From Unit 4, Lesson 14.)

4. To give their animals essential minerals and nutrients, farmers and ranchers often have a block of salt—called "salt lick"—available for their animals to lick.

   a. A rancher is ordering a box of cube-shaped salt licks. The edge lengths of each salt lick are $\frac{5}{12}$ foot. Is the volume of one salt lick greater or less than 1 cubic foot? Explain your reasoning.

   b. The box that contains the salt lick is $1\frac{1}{4}$ feet by $1\frac{2}{3}$ feet by $\frac{5}{6}$ feet. How many cubes of salt lick fit in the box? Explain or show your reasoning.

5. a. How many groups of $\frac{1}{3}$ inch are in $\frac{3}{4}$ inch?

   b. How many inches are in $1\frac{2}{5}$ groups of $1\frac{2}{3}$ inches?

(From Unit 4, Lesson 12.)

6. Here is a table that shows the ratio of flour to water in an art paste. Complete the table with values in equivalent ratios.

| cups of flour | cups of water |
|---|---|
| 1 | $\frac{1}{2}$ |
| 4 | |
| | 3 |
| $\frac{1}{2}$ | |

(From Unit 2, Lesson 12.)

iM KH

# Lesson 16: Solving Problems Involving Fractions

Let's add, subtract, multiply, and divide fractions.

## 16.1: Operations with Fractions

Without calculating, order the expressions according to their values from least to greatest. Be prepared to explain your reasoning.

$\frac{3}{4} + \frac{2}{3}$    $\frac{3}{4} - \frac{2}{3}$    $\frac{3}{4} \cdot \frac{2}{3}$    $\frac{3}{4} \div \frac{2}{3}$

## 16.2: Situations with $\frac{3}{4}$ and $\frac{1}{2}$

Here are four situations that involve $\frac{3}{4}$ and $\frac{1}{2}$.

- Before calculating, decide if each answer is greater than 1 or less than 1.
- Write a multiplication equation or division equation for the situation.
- Answer the question. Show your reasoning. Draw a tape diagram, if needed.

1. There was $\frac{3}{4}$ liter of water in Andre's water bottle. Andre drank $\frac{1}{2}$ of the water. How many liters of water did he drink?

2. The distance from Han's house to his school is $\frac{3}{4}$ kilometers. Han walked $\frac{1}{2}$ kilometers. What fraction of the distance from his house to the school did Han walk?

3. Priya's goal was to collect $\frac{1}{2}$ kilograms of trash. She collected $\frac{3}{4}$ kilograms of trash. How many times her goal was the amount of trash she collected?

4. Mai's class volunteered to clean a park with an area of $\frac{1}{2}$ square mile. Before they took a lunch break, the class had cleaned $\frac{3}{4}$ of the park. How many square miles had they cleaned before lunch?

## 16.3: Pairs of Problems

1. Work with a partner to write equations for the following questions. One person works on the questions labeled A1, B1, . . . , E1 and the other person works on those labeled A2, B2, . . . , E2.

A1. Lin's bottle holds $3\frac{1}{4}$ cups of water. She drank 1 cup of water. What fraction of the water in the bottle did she drink?

A2. Lin's bottle holds $3\frac{1}{4}$ cups of water. After she drank some, there were $1\frac{1}{2}$ cups of water in the bottle. How many cups did she drink?

B1. Plant A is $\frac{16}{3}$ feet tall. This is $\frac{4}{5}$ as tall as Plant B. How tall is Plant B?

B2. Plant A is $\frac{16}{3}$ feet tall. Plant C is $\frac{4}{5}$ as tall as Plant A. How tall is Plant C?

C1. $\frac{8}{9}$ kilogram of berries is put into a container that already has $\frac{7}{3}$ kilogram of berries. How many kilograms are in the container?

C2. A container with $\frac{8}{9}$ kilogram of berries is $\frac{2}{3}$ full. How many kilograms can the container hold?

D1. The area of a rectangle is $14\frac{1}{2}$ sq cm and one side is $4\frac{1}{2}$ cm. How long is the other side?

D2. The side lengths of a rectangle are $4\frac{1}{2}$ cm and $2\frac{2}{5}$ cm. What is the area of the rectangle?

E1. A stack of magazines is $4\frac{2}{5}$ inches high. The stack needs to fit into a box that is $2\frac{1}{8}$ inches high. How many inches too high is the stack?

E2. A stack of magazines is $4\frac{2}{5}$ inches high. Each magazine is $\frac{2}{5}$-inch thick. How many magazines are in the stack?

iM KH

2. Trade papers with your partner, and check your partner's equations. If you disagree, work to reach an agreement.

3. Your teacher will assign 2 or 3 questions for you to answer. For each question:

    a. Estimate the answer before calculating it.

    b. Find the answer, and show your reasoning.

## 16.4: Baking Cookies

Mai, Kiran, and Clare are baking cookies together. They need $\frac{3}{4}$ cup of flour and $\frac{1}{3}$ cup of butter to make a batch of cookies. They each brought the ingredients they had at home.

- Mai brought 2 cups of flour and $\frac{1}{4}$ cup of butter.
- Kiran brought 1 cup of flour and $\frac{1}{2}$ cup of butter.
- Clare brought $1\frac{1}{4}$ cups of flour and $\frac{3}{4}$ cup of butter.

If the students have plenty of the other ingredients they need (sugar, salt, baking soda, etc.), how many whole batches of cookies can they make? Explain your reasoning.

### Lesson 16 Summary

We can add, subtract, multiply, and divide both whole numbers and fractions. Here is a summary of how we add, subtract, multiply, and divide fractions.

- To add or subtract fractions, we often look for a common denominator so the pieces involved are the same size. This makes it easy to add or subtract the pieces.

$$\frac{3}{2} - \frac{4}{5} = \frac{15}{10} - \frac{8}{10}$$

- To multiply fractions, we often multiply the numerators and the denominators.

$$\frac{3}{8} \cdot \frac{5}{9} = \frac{3 \cdot 5}{8 \cdot 9}$$

- To divide a number by a fraction $\frac{a}{b}$, we can multiply the number by $\frac{b}{a}$, which is the reciprocal of $\frac{a}{b}$.

$$\frac{4}{7} \div \frac{5}{3} = \frac{4}{7} \cdot \frac{3}{5}$$

iM KH

# Lesson 16 Practice Problems

1. An orange has about $\frac{1}{4}$ cup of juice. How many oranges are needed to make $2\frac{1}{2}$ cups of juice? Select **all** the equations that represent this question.

    A. $? \cdot \frac{1}{4} = 2\frac{1}{2}$

    B. $\frac{1}{4} \div 2\frac{1}{2} = ?$

    C. $? \cdot 2\frac{1}{2} = \frac{1}{4}$

    D. $2\frac{1}{2} \div \frac{1}{4} = ?$

2. Mai, Clare, and Tyler are hiking from a parking lot to the summit of a mountain. They pass a sign that gives distances.

    > Parking lot: $\frac{3}{4}$ mile
    > Summit: $1\frac{1}{2}$ miles

    ○ Mai says: "We are one third of the way there."
    ○ Clare says: "We have to go twice as far as we have already gone."
    ○ Tyler says: "The total hike is three times as long as what we have already gone."

    Do you agree with any of them? Explain your reasoning.

3. Priya's cat weighs $5\frac{1}{2}$ pounds and her dog weighs $8\frac{1}{4}$ pounds. First, estimate the number that would comlpete each sentence. Then, calculate the answer. If any of your estimates were not close to the answer, explain why that may be.

   a. The cat is _____ as heavy as the dog.

   b. Their combined weight is _____ pounds.

   c. The dog is _____ pounds heavier than the cat.

4. Before refrigerators existed, some people had blocks of ice delivered to their homes. A delivery wagon had a storage box in the shape of a rectangular prism that was $7\frac{1}{2}$ feet by 6 feet by 6 feet. The cubic ice blocks stored in the box had side lengths $1\frac{1}{2}$ feet. How many ice blocks fit in the storage box?

   A. 270

   B. $3\frac{3}{8}$

   C. 80

   D. 180

   (From Unit 4, Lesson 15.)

5. Fill in the blanks with 0.001, 0.1, 10, or 1000 so that the value of each quotient is in the correct column.

| Close to $\frac{1}{100}$ | Close to 1 | Greater than 100 |
|---|---|---|
| ○ _____ $\div 9$ | ○ _____ $\div 0.12$ | ○ _____ $\div \frac{1}{3}$ |
| ○ $12 \div$ _____ | ○ $\frac{1}{8} \div$ _____ | ○ $700.7 \div$ _____ |

   (From Unit 4, Lesson 1.)

iM KH

6. A school club sold 300 shirts. 31% were sold to fifth graders, 52% were sold to sixth graders, and the rest were sold to teachers. How many shirts were sold to each group—fifth graders, sixth graders, and teachers? Explain or show your reasoning.

(From Unit 3, Lesson 15.)

7. Jada has some pennies and dimes. The ratio of Jada's pennies to dimes is 2 to 3.

   a. From the information given, can you determine how many coins Jada has?

   b. If Jada has 55 coins, how many of each kind of coin does she have?

   c. How much are her coins worth?

(From Unit 2, Lesson 15.)

# Lesson 17: Fitting Boxes into Boxes

Let's use what we learned about fractions to find shipping costs.

## 17.1: Determining Shipping Costs (Part 1)

An artist makes necklaces. She packs each necklace in a small jewelry box that is $1\frac{3}{4}$ inches by $2\frac{1}{4}$ inches by $\frac{3}{4}$ inch.

A department store ordered 270 necklaces. The artist plans to ship the necklaces to the department store using flat-rate shipping boxes from the post office.

1. Consider the problem: Which of the flat-rate boxes should she use to minimize her shipping cost?

   What other information would you need to be able to solve the problem?

2. Discuss this information with your group. Make a plan for using this information to find the most inexpensive way to ship the jewelry boxes. Once you have agreed on a plan, write down the main steps.

## 17.2: Determining Shipping Costs (Part 2)

Work with your group to find the best plan for shipping the boxes of necklaces. Each member of your group should select a different type of flat-rate shipping box and answer the following questions. Recall that each jewelry box is $1\frac{3}{4}$ inches by $2\frac{1}{4}$ inches by $\frac{3}{4}$ inch, and that there are 270 jewelry boxes to be shipped.

For each type of flat-rate shipping box:

1. Find how many jewelry boxes can fit into the box. Explain or show how the jewelry boxes can be packed in the shipping box. Draw a sketch to show your thinking, if needed.

2. Calculate the total cost of shipping all 270 jewelry boxes in shipping boxes of that type. Show your reasoning and organize your work so it can be followed by others.

## 17.3: Determining Shipping Costs (Part 3)

1. Share and discuss your work with the other members of your group. Your teacher will display questions to guide your discussion. Note the feedback from your group so you can use it to revise your work.

2. Using the feedback from your group, revise your work to improve its correctness, clarity, and accuracy. Correct any errors. You may also want to add notes or diagrams, or remove unnecessary information.

3. Which shipping boxes should the artist use? As a group, decide which boxes you recommend for shipping 270 jewelry boxes. Be prepared to share your reasoning.

# Learning Targets

**Lesson 1: Size of Divisor and Size of Quotient**

- When dividing, I know how the size of a divisor affects the quotient.

**Lesson 2: Meanings of Division**

- I can explain how multiplication and division are related.

- I can explain two ways of interpreting a division expression such as $27 \div 3$.

- When given a division equation, I can write a multiplication equation that represents the same situation.

**Lesson 3: Interpreting Division Situations**

- I can create a diagram or write an equation that represents division and multiplication questions.

- I can decide whether a division question is asking "how many groups?" or "how many in each group?".

**Lesson 4: How Many Groups? (Part 1)**

- I can find how many groups there are when the amount in each group is not a whole number.

- I can use diagrams and multiplication and division equations to represent "how many groups?" questions.

**Lesson 5: How Many Groups? (Part 2)**

- I can find how many groups there are when the number of groups and the amount in each group are not whole numbers.

**Lesson 6: Using Diagrams to Find the Number of Groups**

- I can use a tape diagram to represent equal-sized groups and find the number of groups.

## Lesson 7: What Fraction of a Group?

- I can tell when a question is asking for the number of groups and that number is less than 1.

- I can use diagrams and multiplication and division equations to represent and answer "what fraction of a group?" questions.

## Lesson 8: How Much in Each Group? (Part 1)

- I can tell when a question is asking for the amount in one group.

- I can use diagrams and multiplication and division equations to represent and answer "how much in each group?" questions.

## Lesson 9: How Much in Each Group? (Part 2)

- I can find the amount in one group in different real-world situations.

## Lesson 10: Dividing by Unit and Non-Unit Fractions

- I can divide a number by a non-unit fraction $\frac{a}{b}$ by reasoning with the numerator and denominator, which are whole numbers.

- I can divide a number by a unit fraction $\frac{1}{b}$ by reasoning with the denominator, which is a whole number.

## Lesson 11: Using an Algorithm to Divide Fractions

- I can describe and apply a rule to divide numbers by any fraction.

## Lesson 12: Fractional Lengths

- I can use division and multiplication to solve problems involving fractional lengths.

## Lesson 13: Rectangles with Fractional Side Lengths

- I can use division and multiplication to solve problems involving areas of rectangles with fractional side lengths.

## Lesson 14: Fractional Lengths in Triangles and Prisms

- I can explain how to find the volume of a rectangular prism using cubes that have a unit fraction as their edge length.

- I can use division and multiplication to solve problems involving areas of triangles with fractional bases and heights.

- I know how to find the volume of a rectangular prism even when the edge lengths are not whole numbers.

## Lesson 15: Volume of Prisms

- I can solve volume problems that involve fractions.

## Lesson 16: Solving Problems Involving Fractions

- I can use mathematical expressions to represent and solve word problems that involve fractions.

## Lesson 17: Fitting Boxes into Boxes

- I can use multiplication and division of fractions to reason about real-world volume problems.

iM KH

# Illustrative Mathematics®
## LEARN MATH FOR LIFE

# GRADE 6

Unit

5

STUDENT EDITION
Book 2

Kendall Hunt |

# Lesson 1: Using Decimals in a Shopping Context

Let's use what we know about decimals to make shopping decisions.

## 1.1: Snacks from the Concession Stand

Clare went to a concession stand that sells pretzels for $3.25, drinks for $1.85, and bags of popcorn for $0.99 each. She bought at least one of each item and spent no more than $10.

*(handwritten work: 3.25 × 2 = 6.50; 1.85 × 2 = 3.70; 6.50 + 3.70 = 10.20)*

1. Could Clare have purchased 2 pretzels, 2 drinks, and 2 bags of popcorn? Explain your reasoning.

   *No because just of the drink and pretzel is to expensive*

2. Could she have bought 1 pretzel, 1 drink, and 5 bags of popcorn? Explain your reasoning.

   *(handwritten work: 3.25 + 1.85 = 5.10; .99 × 5 = 4.95; 5.10 + 4.95 = 10.05)*

   *No it is 5 cents over.*

## 1.2: Planning a Dinner Party

You are planning a dinner party with a budget of $50 and a menu that consists of 1 main dish, 2 side dishes, and 1 dessert. There will be 8 guests at your party.

Choose your menu items and decide on the quantities to buy so you stay on budget. If you choose meat, fish, or poultry for your main dish, plan to buy at least 0.5 pound per person.

1. The budget is $ _6.25_ per guest.

   *(handwritten work: 8 )50 , 48 )*

2. Use the worksheet to record your choices and estimated costs. Then find the estimated total cost and cost per person. See examples in the first two rows.

| item | quantity needed | advertised price | estimated subtotal ($) | estimated cost per person ($) |
|---|---|---|---|---|
| example main dish: fish | 4 pounds | $6.69 per pound | $4 \cdot 7 = 28$ | $28 \div 8 = 3.50$ |
| example dessert: cupcakes | 8 cupcakes | $2.99 per 6 cupcakes | $2 \cdot 3 = 6$ | $6 \div 8 = 0.75$ |
| main dish: chith | 4 Pounds | 1.99 per Pound | 1.99·4= 7.96 | .98 rh |
| side dish 1: Pichapple | 2 Pineapple | 2.99 per 1 | 5.98 | .74 rs |
| side dish 2: mangos | 4 mangos | 3 for 5.97 1.99 Per1 | 8.98 | 1.1225 |
| dessert: cookies | 4 Packs | 5.99 per Pack | 23.96 | 2.9875 |
| estimated total | | | 46.88 | 5.8450 |

.9875
+.7475
─────
1.7350
+1.1225
────
2.8575
+2.9875
────
5.8450

7.99
× 4
────
.36
3.60
20.00

3. Is your estimated total close to your budget? If so, continue to the next question. If not, revise your menu choices until your estimated total is close to the budget.

5.8460

Unit 5 Lesson 1

121

4. Calculate the actual costs of the two most expensive items and add them. Show your reasoning.

5. How will you know if your total cost for all menu items will or will not exceed your budget? Is there a way to predict this without adding all the exact costs? Explain your reasoning.

**Are you ready for more?**

How much would it cost to plant the grass on a football field? Explain or show your reasoning.

**Lesson 1 Summary**

We often use decimals when dealing with money. In these situations, sometimes we round and make estimates, and other times we calculate the numbers more precisely.

There are many different ways we can add, subtract, multiply, and divide decimals. When we perform these calculations, it is helpful to understand the meanings of the digits in a number and the properties of operations. We will investigate how these understandings help us work with decimals in upcoming lessons.

# Lesson 1 Practice Problems

1. Mai had $14.50. She spent $4.35 at the snack bar and $5.25 at the arcade. What is the exact amount of money Mai has left?

    A. $9.60

    B. $10.60

    C. $4.90

    D. $5.90

2. A large cheese pizza costs $7.50. Diego has $40 to spend on pizzas. How many large cheese pizzas can he afford? Explain or show your reasoning.

3. Tickets to a show cost $5.50 for adults and $4.25 for students. A family is purchasing 2 adult tickets and 3 student tickets.

    a. Estimate the total cost.

    b. What is the exact cost?

    c. If the family pays $25, what is the exact amount of change they should receive?

4. Chicken costs $3.20 per pound, and beef costs $4.59 per pound. Answer each question and show your reasoning.

   a. What is the exact cost of 3 pounds of chicken?

   b. What is the exact cost of 3 pound of beef?

   c. How much more does 3 pounds of beef cost than 3 pounds of chicken?

5.   a. How many $\frac{1}{5}$-liter glasses can Lin fill with a $1\frac{1}{2}$-liter bottle of water?

     b. How many $1\frac{1}{2}$-liter bottles of water does it take to fill a 16-liter jug?

   (From Unit 4, Lesson 16.)

iM KH

6. Let the side length of each small square on the grid represents 1 unit. Draw two different triangles, each with base $5\frac{1}{2}$ units and area $19\frac{1}{4}$ units$^2$.

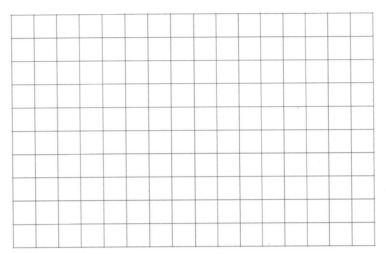

Why does each of your triangles have area $19\frac{1}{4}$ units$^2$? Explain or show your reasoning.

(From Unit 4, Lesson 14.)

7. Find each quotient.

a. $\frac{5}{6} \div \frac{1}{6}$

b. $1\frac{1}{6} \div \frac{1}{12}$

c. $\frac{10}{6} \div \frac{1}{24}$

(From Unit 4, Lesson 10.)

# Lesson 2: Using Diagrams to Represent Addition and Subtraction

Let's represent addition and subtraction of decimals.

## 2.1: Changing Values

1. Here is a rectangle.

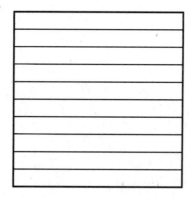

What number does the rectangle represent if each small square represents:

    a. 1

    b. 0.1

    c. 0.01

    d. 0.001

2. Here is a square.

What number does the square represent if each small rectangle represents:

    a. 10

    b. 0.1

    c. 0.00001

iM KH

## 2.2: Squares and Rectangles

You may be familiar with base-ten blocks that represent ones, tens, and hundreds. Here are some diagrams that we will use to represent base-ten units.

- A large square represents 1 one.
- A medium rectangle represents 1 tenth.
- A medium square represents 1 hundredth.
- A small rectangle represents 1 thousandth.
- A small square represents 1 ten-thousandth.

1
one

0.1
tenth

0.01
hundredth

0.001
thousandth

0.0001
ten-thousandth

1. Here is the diagram that Priya drew to represent 0.13. Draw a different diagram that represents 0.13. Explain why both diagrams represent the same number.

2. Here is the diagram that Han drew to represent 0.025. Draw a different diagram that represents 0.025. Explain why both diagrams represent the same number.

3. For each number, draw or describe two different diagrams that represent it.

   a. 0.1

   b. 0.02

   c. 0.004

4. Use diagrams of base-ten units to represent each sum. Think about how you could use as few units as possible to represent each number.

   a. $0.03 + 0.05$ $= 0.08$

   b. $0.006 + 0.007$ $0.013$

   c. $0.4 + 0.7$ $1.1$

iM KH

## 2.3: Finding Sums in Different Ways

1. Here are two ways to calculate the value of $0.26 + 0.07$. In the diagram, each rectangle represents 0.1 and each square represents 0.01.

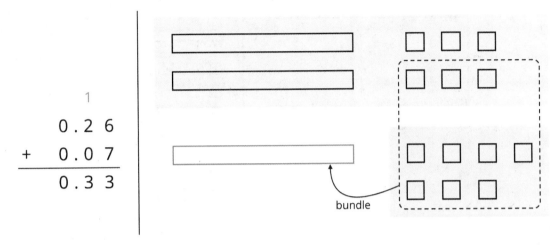

$$
\begin{array}{r}
1\phantom{0000} \\
0.2\,6 \\
+\quad 0.0\,7 \\
\hline
0.3\,3
\end{array}
$$

bundle

Use what you know about base-ten units and addition to explain:

   a. Why ten squares can be "bundled" into a rectangle.

   *10 squares are = to 1 rectangle*

   b. How this "bundling" is represented in the vertical calculation.

   *Every time you carry you are "bundling"*

2. Find the value of $0.38 + 0.69$ by drawing a diagram. Can you find the sum without bundling? Would it be useful to bundle some pieces? Explain your reasoning.

$$
\begin{array}{r}
0.38 \\
+\,0.69 \\
\hline
1.07
\end{array}
$$

3. Calculate $0.38 + 0.69$. Check your calculation against your diagram in the previous question.

4. Find each sum. The larger square represents 1.

a.

$$2.59$$
$$+ \; 0.3122$$
$$\overline{2.9 02}$$

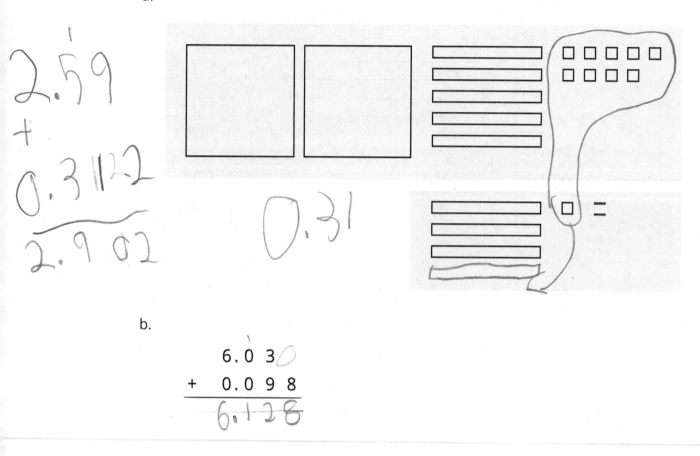

0.31

b.

$$6.0 \; 3\cancel{0}$$
$$+ \; 0.0 \; 9 \; 8$$
$$\overline{6.1 28}$$

## Are you ready for more?

A distant, magical land uses jewels for their bartering system. The jewels are valued and ranked in order of their rarity. Each jewel is worth 3 times the jewel immediately below it in the ranking. The ranking is red, orange, yellow, green, blue, indigo, and violet. So a red jewel is worth 3 orange jewels, a green jewel is worth 3 blue jewels, and so on.

1. If you had 500 violet jewels and wanted to trade so that you carried as few jewels as possible, which jewels would you have?

2. Suppose you have 1 orange jewel, 2 yellow jewels, and 1 indigo jewel. If you're given 2 green jewels and 1 yellow jewels, what is the fewest number of jewels that could represent the value of the jewels you have?

iM KH

## 2.4: Representing Subtraction

1. Here are diagrams that represent differences. Removed pieces are marked with Xs. The larger rectangle represents 1 tenth. For each diagram, write a numerical subtraction expression and determine the value of the expression.

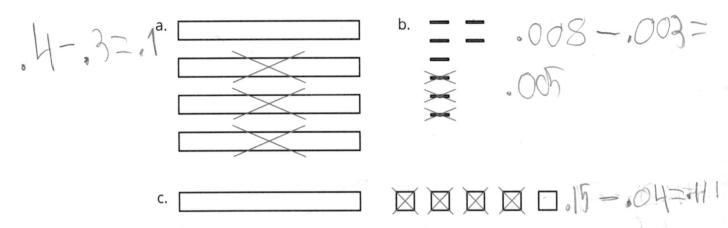

.4 − .3 = .1

a.

b.     .008 − .003 =
       .005

c.      .15 − .04 = .11

2. Express each subtraction in words.

   a. $0.05 - 0.02$ = 0.03

   b. $0.024 - 0.003$ = 0.021

   c. $1.26 - 0.14$ = 1.12

3. Find each difference by drawing a diagram and by calculating with numbers. Make sure the answers from both methods match. If not, check your diagram and your numerical calculation.

   a. $0.05 - 0.02$ = 0.03

   b. $0.024 - 0.003$ = 0.021

   c. $1.26 - 0.14$ = 1.12

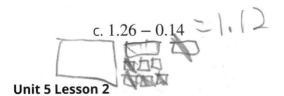

## Lesson 2 Summary

Base-ten diagrams represent collections of base-ten units—tens, ones, tenths, hundredths, etc. We can use them to help us understand sums of decimals.

Suppose we are finding $0.08 + 0.13$. Here is a diagram where a square represents $0.01$ and a rectangle (made up of ten squares) represents $0.1$.

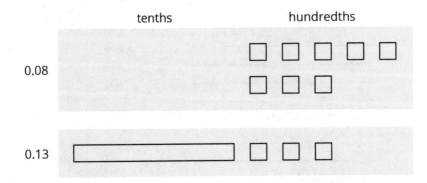

To find the sum, we can "bundle" (or compose) 10 hundredths as 1 tenth.

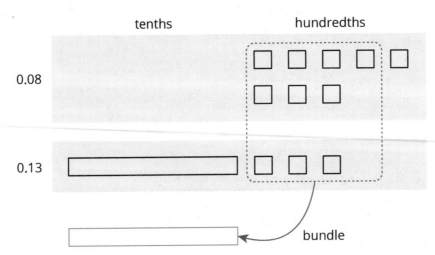

We now have 2 tenths and 1 hundredth, so $0.08 + 0.13 = 0.21$.

0.21

We can also use vertical calculation to find $0.08 + 0.13$.

$$
\begin{array}{r}
\overset{1}{\phantom{0}} \\
0.1\ 3 \\
+\quad 0.0\ 8 \\
\hline
0.2\ 1
\end{array}
$$

Notice how this representation also shows 10 hundredths are bundled (or composed) as 1 tenth.

iM KH

This works for any decimal place. Suppose we are finding $0.008 + 0.013$. Here is a diagram where a small rectangle represents 0.001.

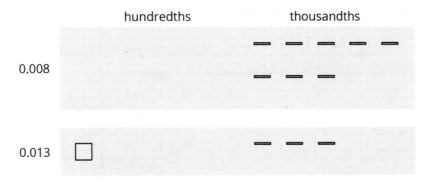

We can "bundle" (or compose) 10 thousandths as 1 hundredth.

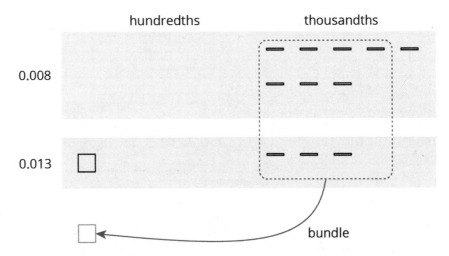

The sum is 2 hundredths and 1 thousandth.

0.021

Here is a vertical calculation of $0.008 + 0.013$.

$$
\begin{array}{r}
1\phantom{00} \\
0.0\ 1\ 3 \\
+\quad 0.0\ 0\ 8 \\
\hline
0.0\ 2\ 1 \\
\end{array}
$$

# Lesson 2 Practice Problems

1. Use the given key to answer the questions.

0.1
tenth

0.01
hundredth

0.001
thousandth

0.0001
ten-thousandth

a. What number does this diagram represent?

b. Draw a diagram that represents 0.216.

c. Draw a diagram that represents 0.304.

2. Here are diagrams that represent 0.137 and 0.284.

|  tenths | hundredths | thousandths |
|---------|------------|-------------|

a. Use the diagram to find the value of $0.137 + 0.284$. Explain your reasoning.

b. Calculate the sum vertically.

$$
\begin{array}{r}
0.1\ 3\ 7 \\
+\ \ 0.2\ 8\ 4 \\
\hline
\end{array}
$$

c. How was your reasoning about $0.137 + 0.284$ the same with the two methods? How was it different?

3. For the first two problems, circle the vertical calculation where digits of the same kind are lined up. Then, finish the calculation and find the sum. For the last two problems, find the sum using vertical calculation.

a. $3.25 + 1$

```
  3.25        3.25        3.25
+  1.0      +  1.0      +      1
———————     ———————     ———————
```

b. $0.5 + 1.15$

```
  0.5         0.5         0.50
+ 1.15      + 1.1 5     + 1.1 50
———————     ———————     ————————
```

c. $10.6 + 1.7$

d. $123 + 0.2$

4. Andre has been practicing his math facts. He can now complete 135 multiplication facts in 90 seconds.

a. If Andre is answering questions at a constant rate, how many facts can he answer per second?

b. Noah also works at a constant rate, and he can complete 75 facts in 1 minute. Who is working faster? Explain or show your reasoning.

(From Unit 2, Lesson 9.)

# Lesson 3: Adding and Subtracting Decimals with Few Non-Zero Digits

Let's add and subtract decimals.

## 3.1: Do the Zeros Matter?

1. Evaluate mentally: $1.009 + 0.391$    1.400

2. Decide if each equation is true or false. Be prepared to explain your reasoning.

   ✓ a. $34.56000 = 34.56$

   ✓ b. $25 = 25.0$

   ✗ c. $2.405 = 2.45$

## 3.2: Calculating Sums

1. Andre and Jada drew base-ten diagrams to represent $0.007 + 0.004$. Andre drew 11 small rectangles. Jada drew only two figures: a square and a small rectangle.

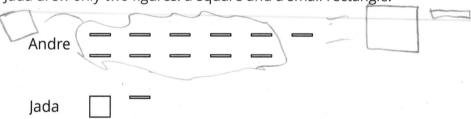

   a. If both students represented the sum correctly, what value does each small rectangle represent? What value does each square represent?

   b. Draw or describe a diagram that could represent the sum $0.008 + 0.07$.

$$\begin{array}{r} + \ 0.008 \\ 0.077 \\ \hline 0.078 \end{array}$$

iM KH

2. Here are two calculations of $0.2 + 0.05$. Which is correct? Explain why one is correct and the other is incorrect.

$\checkmark$

```
    0.2
+  0.05
-------
   0.25
```

```
    0.2
+  0.05
-------
   0.07
```

because They Lined up the desimal point unlike the auther one witchi hot libed up

3. Compute each sum. If you get stuck, consider drawing base-ten diagrams to help you.

a.

```
   0.11
+ 0.005
-------
  0.115
```

b. $0.209 + 0.01$

```
+  0.209
   0.01
-------
  0.219
```

c. $10.2 + 1.1456$

```
   10.2
+  1.1456
--------
  11.3456
```

# 3.3: Subtracting Decimals of Different Lengths

Diego and Noah drew different diagrams to represent 0.4 − 0.03. Each rectangle represents 0.1. Each square represents 0.01.

- Diego started by drawing 4 rectangles to represent 0.4. He then replaced 1 rectangle with 10 squares and crossed out 3 squares to represent subtraction of 0.03, leaving 3 rectangles and 7 squares in his diagram.

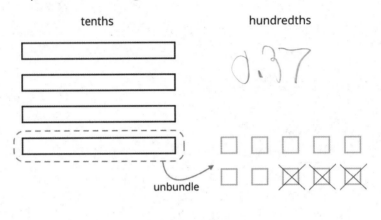

Diego's Method

- Noah started by drawing 4 rectangles to represent 0.4. He then crossed out 3 rectangles to represent the subtraction, leaving 1 rectangle in his diagram.

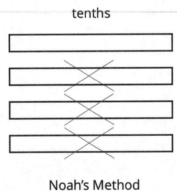

Noah's Method

1. Do you agree that either diagram correctly represents 0.4 − 0.03? Discuss your reasoning with a partner.

iM KH

2. Elena also drew a diagram to represent $0.4 - 0.03$. She started by drawing 4 rectangles. She then replaced all 4 rectangles with 40 squares and crossed out 3 squares to represent subtraction of 0.03, leaving 37 squares in her diagram. Is her diagram correct? Discuss your reasoning with a partner.

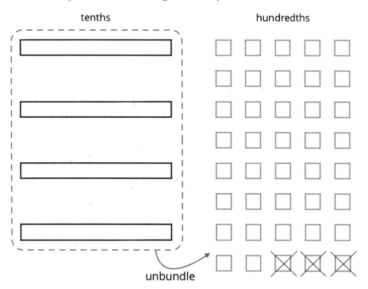

Elena's Method

3. Find each difference. Explain or show your reasoning.

   a. $0.3 - 0.05$

   b. $2.1 - 0.4$

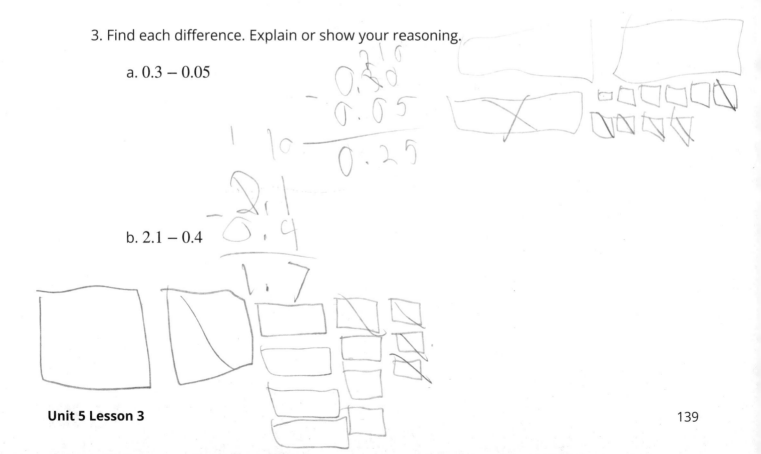

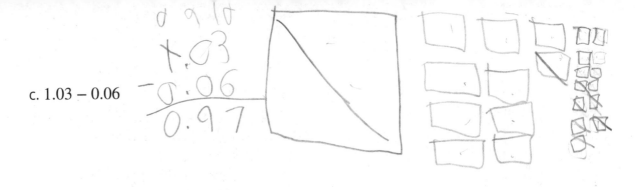

c. 1.03 − 0.06

$$\begin{array}{r} \overset{0}{\cancel{1}}\overset{9}{.}\overset{10}{\cancel{0}}3 \\ -\ 0.06 \\ \hline 0.97 \end{array}$$

d. 0.02 − 0.007

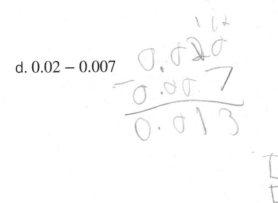

$$\begin{array}{r} 0.0\overset{1}{\cancel{2}}\overset{10}{\cancel{0}} \\ -\ 0.007 \\ \hline 0.013 \end{array}$$

## Are you ready for more?

A distant, magical land uses jewels for their bartering system. The jewels are valued and ranked in order of their rarity. Each jewel is worth 3 times the jewel immediately below it in the ranking. The ranking is red, orange, yellow, green, blue, indigo, and violet. So a red jewel is worth 3 orange jewels, a green jewel is worth 3 blue jewels, and so on.

At the Auld Shoppe, a shopper buys items that are worth 2 yellow jewels, 2 green jewels, 2 blue jewels, and 1 indigo jewel. If they came into the store with 1 red jewel, 1 yellow jewel, 2 green jewels, 1 blue jewel, and 2 violet jewels, what jewels do they leave with? Assume the shopkeeper gives them their change using as few jewels as possible.

iM KH

## Lesson 3 Summary

Base-ten diagrams can help us understand subtraction as well. Suppose we are finding $0.23 - 0.07$. Here is a diagram showing 0.23, or 2 tenths and 3 hundredths.

Subtracting 7 hundredths means removing 7 small squares, but we do not have enough to remove. Because 1 tenth is equal to 10 hundredths, we can "unbundle" (or decompose) one of the tenths (1 rectangle) into 10 hundredths (10 small squares).

We now have 1 tenth and 13 hundredths, from which we can remove 7 hundredths.

We have 1 tenth and 6 hundredths remaining, so $0.23 - 0.07 = 0.16$.

Here is a vertical calculation of $0.23 - 0.07$.

$$\begin{array}{r} {\scriptstyle 1\ \ 13} \\ 0.\cancel{2}\,\cancel{3} \\ -\ \ 0.0\ 7 \\ \hline 0.1\ 6 \end{array}$$

Notice how this representation also shows a tenth is unbundled (or decomposed) into 10 hundredths in order to subtract 7 hundredths.

This works for any decimal place. Suppose we are finding $0.023 - 0.007$. Here is a diagram showing 0.023.

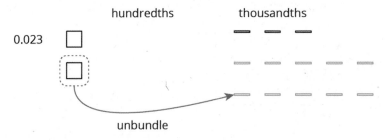

We want to remove 7 thousandths (7 small rectangles). We can "unbundle" (or decompose) one of the hundredths into 10 thousandths.

Now we can remove 7 thousandths.

We have 1 hundredth and 6 thousandths remaining, so $0.023 - 0.007 = 0.016$.

Here is a vertical calculation of $0.023 - 0.007$.

$$
\begin{array}{r}
\overset{1}{\phantom{0.0}}\overset{13}{\phantom{2}} \\
0.0\ \cancel{2}\ \cancel{3} \\
-\quad 0.0\ 0\ 7 \\
\hline
0.0\ 1\ 6
\end{array}
$$

iM KH

# Lesson 3 Practice Problems

1. Here is a base-ten diagram that represents 1.13. Use the diagram to find $1.13 - 0.46$.

   Explain or show your reasoning.

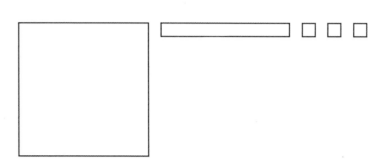

2. Compute the following sums. If you get stuck, consider drawing base-ten diagrams.

   a. $0.027 + 0.004$

   b. $0.203 + 0.01$

   c. $1.2 + 0.145$

3. A student said we cannot subtract 1.97 from 20 because 1.97 has two decimal digits and 20 has none. Do you agree with him? Explain or show your reasoning.

4. Decide which calculation shows the correct way to find $0.3 - 0.006$ and explain your reasoning.

A
```
    0 . 3
 - 0.0 0 6
_____
   0 . 3 0 6
```

B
```
    0 . 3
 - 0.0 0 6
_____
   0 . 0 9 7
```

C
```
    0 . 3 0
 - 0.0  0 6
_____
   0 . 0 2 4
```

D
```
    0 . 3 0 0
 - 0.0  0 6
_____
   0 . 2 9 4
```

5. Complete the calculations so that each shows the correct difference.

a.
```
    1 4 2 . 6
 -      1 . 4
_____
  ☐ ☐ ☐ . 2
```

b.
```
    3 8 . 6 0
 -   6 . 7 5
_____
  ☐ ☐ . ☐ 5
```

c.
```
    2 4 1 . 7 6
 -      2 . 1 8
_____
  ☐ ☐ ☐ . ☐ 8
```

6. The school store sells pencils for $0.30 each, hats for $14.50 each, and binders for $3.20 each. Elena would like to buy 3 pencils, a hat, and 2 binders. She estimated that the cost will be less than $20.

a. Do you agree with her estimate? Explain your reasoning.

b. Estimate the number of pencils could she buy with $5. Explain or show your reasoning.

(From Unit 5, Lesson 1.)

iM KH

7. A rectangular prism measures $7\frac{1}{2}$ cm by 12 cm by $15\frac{1}{2}$ cm.

  a. Calculate the number of cubes with edge length $\frac{1}{2}$ cm that fit in this prism.

  b. What is the volume of the prism in $cm^3$? Show your reasoning. If you are stuck, think about how many cubes with $\frac{1}{2}$-cm edge lengths fit into $1\ cm^3$.

(From Unit 4, Lesson 15.)

8. At a constant speed, a car travels 75 miles in 60 minutes. How far does the car travel in 18 minutes? If you get stuck, consider using the table.

| minutes | distance in miles |
|---------|-------------------|
| 60      | 75                |
| 6       |                   |
| 18      |                   |

(From Unit 2, Lesson 12.)

# Lesson 4: Adding and Subtracting Decimals with Many Non-Zero Digits

Let's practice adding and subtracting decimals.

## 4.1: The Cost of a Photo Print

1. Here are three ways to write a subtraction calculation. What do you notice? What do you wonder?

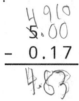

$$\begin{array}{r} 4\,9\,10 \\ 5.00 \\ -\ 0.17 \\ \hline 4.83 \end{array}$$

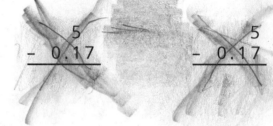

2. Clare bought a photo for 17 cents and paid with a $5 bill. Look at the previous question. Which way of writing the numbers could Clare use to find the change she should receive? Be prepared to explain how you know.

3. Find the amount of change that Clare should receive. Show your reasoning, and be prepared to explain how you calculate the difference of 0.17 and 5.

iM KH

## 4.2: Decimals All Around

1. Find the value of each expression. Show your reasoning.

   a. $11.3 - 9.5$

   $$\begin{array}{r} 1\!\!\!\;^{10}\,1.3 \\ -\ 9.5 \\ \hline 1.8 \end{array}$$

   $1.8$

   b. $318.8 - 94.63$

   $$\begin{array}{r} 2\,6\quad 7\,10 \\ 3\,1\,8.8\,0 \\ -\ 94.63 \\ \hline 224.17 \end{array}$$

   $224.17$

   c. $0.02 - 0.0116$

   $$\begin{array}{r} 1\,9\,10 \\ 0.0\,2\,0\,0 \\ -\ 0.0116 \\ \hline 0.0084 \end{array}$$

   $0.0084$

2. Discuss with a partner:

   o Which method or methods did you use in the previous question? Why?

   o In what ways were your methods effective? Was there an expression for which your methods did not work as well as expected?

3. Lin's grandmother ordered needles that were 0.3125 inches long to administer her medication, but the pharmacist sent her needles that were 0.6875 inches long. How much longer were these needles than the ones she ordered? Show your reasoning.

   $$\begin{array}{r} 0.6875 \\ -\ 0.3125 \\ \hline 0.3750 \end{array}$$

4. There is 0.162 liter of water in a 1-liter bottle. How much more water should be put in the bottle so it contains exactly 1 liter? Show your reasoning.

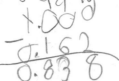

5. One micrometer is 1 millionth of a meter. A red blood cell is about 7.5 micrometers in diameter. A coarse grain of sand is about 70 micrometers in diameter. Find the difference between the two diameters in *meters*. Show your reasoning.

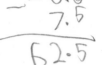

## 4.3: Missing Numbers

Write the missing digits in each calculation so that the value of each sum or difference is correct. Be prepared to explain your reasoning.

1.

$$\begin{array}{r} 0.4\ 0\ 4 \\ +\ \boxed{\phantom{0}\ \phantom{0}\ \phantom{0}\ \phantom{0}} \\ \hline 1\phantom{.000} \end{array}$$

2.

$$\begin{array}{r} 9.8\ 7\ 6\ 5 \\ +\ \boxed{\phantom{0}\ \phantom{0}\ \phantom{0}\ \phantom{0}\ \phantom{0}} \\ \hline 1\ 0\phantom{.000} \end{array}$$

3.

$$\begin{array}{r} 0.7 \\ -\ \boxed{\phantom{0}\ \phantom{0}\ \phantom{0}\ \phantom{0}} \\ \hline 0.0\ 1\ 2 \end{array}$$

4.

$$\begin{array}{r} 7 \\ -\ \boxed{\phantom{0}\ \phantom{0}\ \phantom{0}\ \phantom{0}} \\ \hline 3.4\ 5\ 6\ 7 \end{array}$$

5.

$$\begin{array}{r} 7\ 0 \\ -\ \boxed{\phantom{0}\ \phantom{0}\ \phantom{0}\ \phantom{0}\ \phantom{0}} \\ \hline 0.0\ 0\ 8\ 9 \end{array}$$

iM KH

## Are you ready for more?

In a cryptarithmetic puzzle, the digits 0-9 are represented using the first 10 letters of the alphabet. Use your understanding of decimal addition to determine which digits go with the letters A, B, C, D, E, F, G, H, I, and J. How many possibilities can you find?

```
   I H F . I J
 + J I I . F I
 ─────────────
   E J I . I E
```

## Lesson 4 Summary

Base-ten diagrams work best for representing subtraction of numbers with few non-zero digits, such as $0.16 - 0.09$. For numbers with many non-zero digits, such as $0.25103 - 0.04671$, it would take a long time to draw the base-ten diagram. With vertical calculations, we can find this difference efficiently.

Thinking about base-ten diagrams can help us make sense of this calculation.

```
              10
         4  ∅  10
   0 . 2  5̸  1̸  ∅̸  3
 − 0 . 0  4  6   7   1
 ──────────────────────
   0 . 2  0  4   3   2
```

The thousandth in 0.25103 is unbundled (or decomposed) to make 10 ten-thousandths so that we can subtract 7 ten-thousandths. Similarly, one of the hundredths in 0.25103 is unbundled (or decomposed) to make 10 thousandths.

# Lesson 4 Practice Problems

1. For each subtraction problem, circle the correct calculation.

   a. $7.2 - 3.67$

   a.

   | | | |
   |---|---|---|
   | 7 . 2 | 0 7 . 2 | 7 . 2 0 |
   | $-$ 3 . 6 7 | $-$ 3 . 6 7 | $-$ 3 . 6 7 |
   | 3 . 0 5 | 3 . 0 5 | 3 . 5 3 |

   b. $16 - 1.4$

   b.

   | | | |
   |---|---|---|
   | 1 6 | 1 6 . 0 | 16 . 0 |
   | $-$ 1 . 4 | $-$ 1 . 4 0 | $-$ 1 . 4 |
   | 0 . 2 | 0 . 2 0 | 14 . 6 |

2. Explain how you could find the difference of 1 and 0.1978.

   $$\begin{array}{r} {}^{0}{\cancel{1}}.{}^{9}{\cancel{0}}{}^{9}{\cancel{0}}{}^{9}{\cancel{0}}{}^{10}{\cancel{0}} \\ - \ 0.1978 \\ \hline 0.8022 \end{array}$$

3. A bag of chocolates is labeled to contain 0.384 pound of chocolates. The actual weight of the chocolates is 0.3798 pound.

   a. Are the chocolates heavier or lighter than the weight stated on the label? Explain how you know.

   b. How much heavier or lighter are the chocolates than stated on the label? Show your reasoning.

4. Complete the calculations so that each shows the correct sum.

   a.

   ```
     1 . 0 3 6
   + [ ][ ][ ][ ]
   ─────────────
       4
   ```

   b.

   ```
     0 . 7 3 8
   + [ ][ ][ ][ ]
   ─────────────
       1
   ```

   c.

   ```
     0 . 5 1 3 7
   + [ ][ ][ ][ ]
   ─────────────
       1
   ```

iM KH

5. A shipping company is loading cube-shaped crates into a larger cube-shaped container. The smaller cubes have side lengths of $2\frac{1}{2}$ feet, and the larger shipping container has side lengths of 10 feet. How many crates will fit in the large shipping container? Explain your reasoning.

(From Unit 4, Lesson 14.)

6. For every 9 customers, the chef prepares 2 loaves of bread.

  a. Here is double number line showing varying numbers of customers and the loaves prepared. Complete the missing information.

  b. The same information is shown on a table. Complete the missing information.

| customers | loaves |
|-----------|--------|
| 9 | 2 |
|   | 4 |
| 27 |   |
|   | 14 |
| 1 |   |

  c. Use either representation to answer these questions.

  ○ How many loaves are needed for 63 customers?

  ○ How many customers are there if the chef prepares 20 loaves?

  ○ How much of a loaf is prepared for each customer?

(From Unit 2, Lesson 13.)

# Lesson 5: Decimal Points in Products

Let's look at products that are decimals.

## 5.1: Multiplying by 10

1. In which equation is the value of $x$ the largest?

$81$ $x \cdot 10 = 810$     $8.1$ $x \cdot 10 = 81$     $.81$ $x \cdot 10 = 8.1$     $081$ $x \cdot 10 = 0.81$

2. How many times the size of 0.81 is 810?

1000 ✗ greater

## 5.2: Fractionally Speaking: Powers of Ten

Work with a partner. One person solves the problems labeled "Partner A" and the other person solves those labeled "Partner B." Then compare your results.

1. Find each product or quotient. Be prepared to explain your reasoning.

Partner A

a. $250 \cdot \frac{1}{10}$ = 25

b. $250 \cdot \frac{1}{100}$ 2.5

c. $48 \div 10$ 4.8

d. $48 \div 100$, 48

Partner B

a. $250 \div 10$ 25

b. $250 \div 100$ 2.5

c. $48 \cdot \frac{1}{10}$ 4.8

d. $48 \cdot \frac{1}{100}$ .48

2. Use your work in the previous problems to find $720 \cdot (0.1)$ and $720 \cdot (0.01)$. Explain your reasoning.

72.0     7.2

Pause here for a class discussion.

iM KH

3. Find each product. Show your reasoning.

a. $36 \cdot (0.1)$ $\frac{1}{10}$ 3.6

b. $(24.5) \cdot (0.1)$ $\frac{1}{10}$ 2.45

c. $(1.8) \cdot (0.1)$ $\frac{1}{10}$ .18

d. $54 \cdot (0.01)$ $\frac{1}{100}$ .54

e. $(9.2) \cdot (0.01)$ $\frac{1}{100}$ .092

4. Jada says: "If you multiply a number by 0.001, the decimal point of the number moves three places to the left." Do you agree with her? Explain your reasoning.

Yes beacse when multiplying it moves to the Left.

# 5.3: Fractionally Speaking: Multiples of Powers of Ten

1. Select **all** expressions that are equivalent to $(0.6) \cdot (0.5)$. Be prepared to explain your reasoning.

   a. $6 \cdot (0.1) \cdot 5 \cdot (0.1)$

   b. $6 \cdot (0.01) \cdot 5 \cdot (0.1)$

   c. $6 \cdot \frac{1}{10} \cdot 5 \cdot \frac{1}{10}$

   d. $6 \cdot \frac{1}{1,000} \cdot 5 \cdot \frac{1}{100}$

   e. $6 \cdot (0.001) \cdot 5 \cdot (0.01)$

   f. $6 \cdot 5 \cdot \frac{1}{10} \cdot \frac{1}{10}$

   g. $\frac{6}{10} \cdot \frac{5}{10}$

2. Find the value of $(0.6) \cdot (0.5)$. Show your reasoning.

3. Find the value of each product by writing and reasoning with an equivalent expression with fractions.

   a. $(0.3) \cdot (0.02)$

   b. $(0.7) \cdot (0.05)$

iM KH

**Are you ready for more?**

Ancient Romans used the letter I for 1, V for 5, X for 10, L for 50, C for 100, D for 500, and M for 1,000. Write a problem involving merchants at an agora, an open-air market, that uses multiplication of numbers written with Roman numerals.

## Lesson 5 Summary

We can use fractions like $\frac{1}{10}$ and $\frac{1}{100}$ to reason about the location of the decimal point in a product of two decimals.

Let's take $24 \cdot (0.1)$ as an example. There are several ways to find the product:

- We can interpret it as 24 groups of 1 tenth (or 24 tenths), which is 2.4.
- We can think of it as $24 \cdot \frac{1}{10}$, which is equal to $\frac{24}{10}$ (and also equal to 2.4).
- Multiplying by $\frac{1}{10}$ has the same result as dividing by 10, so we can also think of the product as $24 \div 10$, which is equal to 2.4.

Similarly, we can think of $(0.7) \cdot (0.09)$ as 7 tenths times 9 hundredths, and write:

$$\left(7 \cdot \frac{1}{10}\right) \cdot \left(9 \cdot \frac{1}{100}\right)$$

We can rearrange whole numbers and fractions:

$$(7 \cdot 9) \cdot \left(\frac{1}{10} \cdot \frac{1}{100}\right)$$

This tells us that $(0.7) \cdot (0.09) = 0.063$.

$$63 \cdot \frac{1}{1,000} = \frac{63}{1,000}$$

Here is another example: To find $(1.5) \cdot (0.43)$, we can think of 1.5 as 15 tenths and 0.43 as 43 hundredths. We can write the tenths and hundredths as fractions and rearrange the factors.

$$\left(15 \cdot \frac{1}{10}\right) \cdot \left(43 \cdot \frac{1}{100}\right) = 15 \cdot 43 \cdot \frac{1}{1,000}$$

Multiplying 15 and 43 gives us 645, and multiplying $\frac{1}{10}$ and $\frac{1}{100}$ gives us $\frac{1}{1,000}$. So $(1.5) \cdot (0.43)$ is $645 \cdot \frac{1}{1,000}$, which is 0.645.

# Lesson 5 Practice Problems

1.  a. Find the product of each number and $\frac{1}{100}$.

    122.1           11.8           1350.1           1.704

    b. What happens to the decimal point of the original number when you multiply it by $\frac{1}{100}$? Why do you think that is? Explain your reasoning.

2. Which expression has the same value as $(0.06) \cdot (0.154)$? Select **all** that apply.

    A. $6 \cdot \frac{1}{100} \cdot 154 \cdot \frac{1}{1,000}$

    B. $6 \cdot 154 \cdot \frac{1}{100,000}$

    C. $6 \cdot (0.1) \cdot 154 \cdot (0.01)$

    D. $6 \cdot 154 \cdot (0.00001)$

    E. $0.00924$

3. Calculate the value of each expression by writing the decimal factors as fractions, then writing their product as a decimal. Show your reasoning.

    a. $(0.01) \cdot (0.02)$

    b. $(0.3) \cdot (0.2)$

    c. $(1.2) \cdot 5$

    d. $(0.9) \cdot (1.1)$

    e. $(1.5) \cdot 2$

4. Write three numerical expressions that are equivalent to $(0.0004) \cdot (0.005)$.

5. Calculate each sum.

   a. $33.1 + 1.95$          a. $1.075 + 27.105$          a. $0.401 + 9.28$

(From Unit 5, Lesson 3.)

6. Calculate each difference. Show your reasoning.

   a. $13.2 - 1.78$          a. $23.11 - 0.376$          a. $0.9 - 0.245$

(From Unit 5, Lesson 4.)

7. On the grid, draw a quadrilateral *that is not a rectangle* that has an area of 18 square units. Show how you know the area is 18 square units.

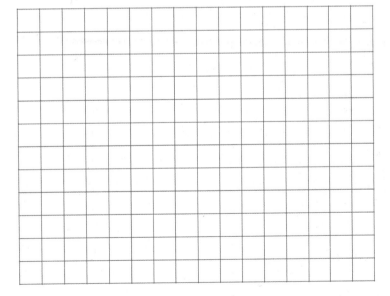

(From Unit 1, Lesson 3.)

# Lesson 6: Methods for Multiplying Decimals

Let's look at some ways we can represent multiplication of decimals.

## 6.1: Equivalent Expressions

Write as many expressions as you can think of that are equal to 0.6. Do not use addition or subtraction.

## 6.2: Using Properties of Numbers to Reason about Multiplication

Elena and Noah used different methods to compute $(0.23) \cdot (1.5)$. Both calculations were correct.

| Elena's Method | Noah's Method |
|---|---|
| $(0.23) \cdot 100 = 23$ | $0.23 = \frac{23}{100}$ |
| $(1.5) \cdot 10 = 15$ | $1.5 = \frac{15}{10}$ |
| $23 \cdot 15 = 345$ | $\frac{23}{100} \cdot \frac{15}{10} = \frac{345}{1,000}$ |
| $345 \div 1,000 = 0.345$ | $\frac{345}{1,000} = 0.345$ |

1. Analyze the two methods, then discuss these questions with your partner.

   ○ Which method makes more sense to you? Why?

   ○ What might Elena do to compute $(0.16) \cdot (0.03)$? What might Noah do to compute $(0.16) \cdot (0.03)$? Will the two methods result in the same value?

2. Compute each product using the equation $21 \cdot 47 = 987$ and what you know about fractions, decimals, and place value. Explain or show your reasoning.

   a. $(2.1) \cdot (4.7)$

   b. $21 \cdot (0.047)$

   c. $(0.021) \cdot (4.7)$

# 6.3: Using Area Diagrams to Reason about Multiplication

1. In the diagram, the side length of each square is 0.1 unit.

   a. Explain why the area of each square is *not* 0.1 square unit.

   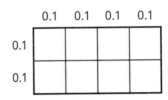

   b. How can you use the area of each square to find the area of the rectangle? Explain or show your reasoning.

   c. Explain how the diagram shows that the equation $(0.4) \cdot (0.2) = 0.08$ is true.

2. Label the squares with their side lengths so the area of this rectangle represents $40 \cdot 20$.

   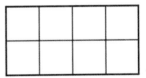

   a. What is the area of each square?

   b. Use the squares to help you find $40 \cdot 20$. Explain or show your reasoning.

3. Label the squares with their side lengths so the area of this rectangle represents $(0.04) \cdot (0.02)$.

   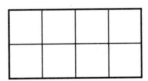

   Next, use the diagram to help you find $(0.04) \cdot (0.02)$. Explain or show your reasoning.

**Lesson 6 Summary**

Here are three other ways to calculate a product of two decimals such as $(0.04) \cdot (0.07)$.

- First, we can multiply each decimal by the same power of 10 to obtain whole-number factors.

$$(0.04) \cdot 100 = 4$$

$$(0.07) \cdot 100 = 7$$

$$4 \cdot 7 = 28$$

  Because we multiplied both 0.04 and 0.07 by 100 to get 4 and 7, the product 28 is $(100 \cdot 100)$ times the original product, so we need to divide 28 by 10,000.

$$28 \div 10,000 = 0.0028$$

- Second, we can write each decimal as a fraction, $0.04 = \frac{4}{100}$ and $0.07 = \frac{7}{100}$, and multiply them.

$$\frac{4}{100} \cdot \frac{7}{100} = \frac{28}{10,000} = 0.0028$$

- Third, we can use an area model. The product $(0.04) \cdot (0.07)$ can be thought of as the area of a rectangle with side lengths of 0.04 unit and 0.07 unit.

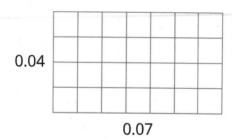

0.04

0.07

In this diagram, each small square is 0.01 unit by 0.01 unit. The area of each square, in square units, is therefore $\left(\frac{1}{100} \cdot \frac{1}{100}\right)$, which is $\frac{1}{10,000}$.

Because the rectangle is composed of 28 small squares, the area of the rectangle, in square units, must be:

$$28 \cdot \frac{1}{10,000} = \frac{28}{10,000} = 0.0028$$

All three calculations show that $(0.04) \cdot (0.07) = 0.0028$.

iM KH

# Lesson 6 Practice Problems

1. Find each product. Show your reasoning.

   a. $(1.2) \cdot (0.11)$

   b. $(0.34) \cdot (0.02)$

   c. $120 \cdot (0.002)$

2. You can use a rectangle to represent $(0.3) \cdot (0.5)$.

   a. What must the side length of each square represent for the rectangle to correctly represent $(0.3) \cdot (0.5)$?

   b. What area is represented by each square?

   c. What is $(0.3) \cdot (0.5)$? Show your reasoning.

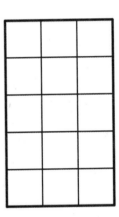

3. One gallon of gasoline in Buffalo, New York costs $2.29. In Toronto, Canada, one liter of gasoline costs $0.91. There are 3.8 liters in one gallon.

   a. How much does one gallon of gas cost in Toronto? Round your answer to the nearest cent.

   b. Is the cost of gas greater in Buffalo or in Toronto? How much greater?

4. Calculate each sum or difference.

$$10.3 + 3.7 \qquad 20.99 - 4.97 \qquad 15.99 + 23.51 \qquad 1.893 - 0.353$$

(From Unit 5, Lesson 2.)

5. Find the value of $\frac{49}{50} \div \frac{7}{6}$ using any method.

(From Unit 4, Lesson 11.)

6. Find the area of the shaded region. All angles are right angles. Show your reasoning.

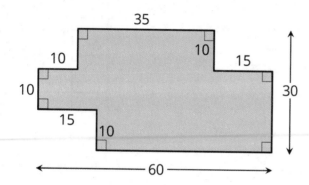

(From Unit 1, Lesson 1.)

7.   a. Priya finds $(1.05) \cdot (2.8)$ by calculating $105 \cdot 28$, then moving the decimal point three places to the left. Why does Priya's method make sense?

   b. Use Priya's method to calculate $(1.05) \cdot (2.8)$. You can use the fact that $105 \cdot 28 = 2{,}940$.

   c. Use Priya's method to calculate $(0.0015) \cdot (0.024)$.

iM KH

# Lesson 7: Using Diagrams to Represent Multiplication

Let's use area diagrams to find products.

## 7.1: Estimate the Product

For each of the following products, choose the best estimate of its value. Be prepared to explain your reasoning.

1. $(6.8) \cdot (2.3)$

    ○ 1.40

    ○ 14

    ○ 140

2. $74 \cdot (8.1)$

    ○ 5.6

    ○ 56

    ○ 560

3. $166 \cdot (0.09)$

    ○ 1.66

    ○ 16.6

    ○ 166

4. $(3.4) \cdot (1.9)$

    ○ 6.5

    ○ 65

    ○ 650

## 7.2: Connecting Area Diagrams to Calculations with Whole Numbers

1. Here are three ways of finding the area of a rectangle that is 24 units by 13 units.

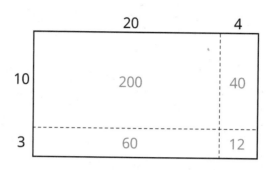

Diagram 1

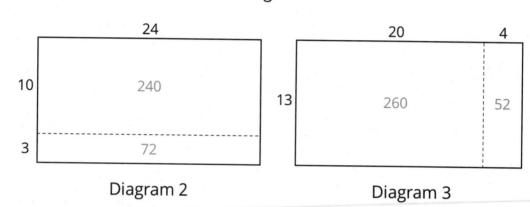

Diagram 2                    Diagram 3

a. What do the diagrams have in common? How are they the same?

b. How are the diagrams different?

c. If you were to find the area of a rectangle that is 37 units by 19 units, which of the three ways of decomposing the rectangle would you use? Why?

iM KH

2. You may be familiar with different ways to write multiplication calculations. Here are two ways to calculate 24 times 13.

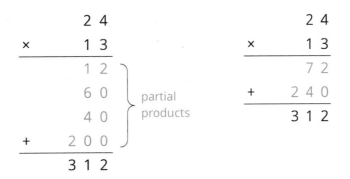

Calculation A                    Calculation B

a. In Calculation A, how are each of the partial products obtained? For instance, where does the 12 come from?

b. In Calculation B, how are the 72 and 240 obtained?

c. Look at the diagrams in the first question. Which diagram corresponds to Calculation A? Which one corresponds to Calculation B?

d. How are the partial products in Calculation A and the 72 and 240 in Calculation B related to the numbers in the diagrams?

3. Use the two following methods to find the product of 18 and 14.

   ○ Calculate numerically.

   ○ Here is a rectangle that is 18 units by 14 units. Find its area, in square units, by decomposing it. Show your reasoning.

$$\begin{array}{r} 1\ 8 \\ \times\quad 1\ 4 \\ \hline \end{array}$$

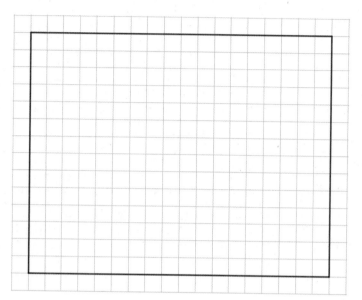

4. Compare the values of 18 · 14 that you obtained using the two methods. If they are not the same, check your work.

## 7.3: Connecting Area Diagrams to Calculations with Decimals

1. You can use area diagrams to represent products of decimals. Here is an area diagram that represents (2.4) · (1.3).

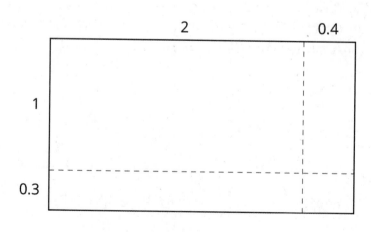

   a. Find the region that represents (0.4) · (0.3). Label it with its area of 0.12.

   b. Label the other regions with their areas.

   c. Find the value of (2.4) · (1.3). Show your reasoning.

iM KH

2. Here are two ways of calculating $(2.4) \cdot (1.3)$.

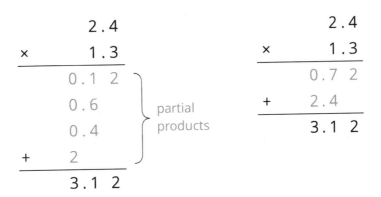

Calculation A

Calculation B

Analyze the calculations and discuss these questions with a partner:

- In Calculation A, where does the 0.12 and other partial products come from?
- In Calculation B, where do the 0.72 and 2.4 come from?
- In each calculation, why are the numbers below the horizontal line aligned vertically the way they are?

3. Find the product of $(3.1) \cdot (1.5)$ by drawing and labeling an area diagram. Show your reasoning.

4. Show how to calculate $(3.1) \cdot (1.5)$ using numbers without a diagram. Be prepared to explain your reasoning. If you are stuck, use the examples in a previous question to help you.

**Are you ready for more?**

How many hectares is the property of your school? How many morgens is that?

# 7.4: Using the Partial Products Method

1. Label the area diagram to represent $(2.5) \cdot (1.2)$ and to find that product.

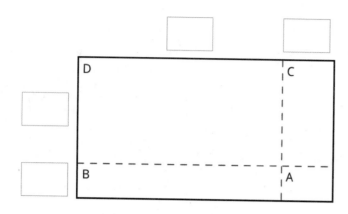

a. Decompose each number into its base-ten units (ones, tenths, etc.) and write them in the boxes on each side of the rectangle.

b. Label Regions A, B, C, and D with their areas. Show your reasoning.

c. Find the product that the area diagram represents. Show your reasoning.

2. Here are two ways to calculate $(2.5) \cdot (1.2)$. Each number with a box gives the area of one or more regions in the area diagram.

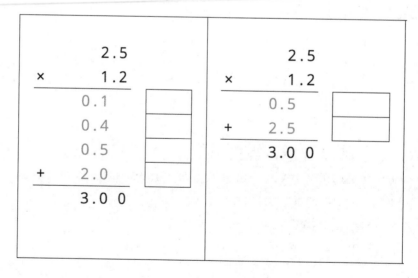

Calculation A          Calculation B

a. In the boxes next to each number, write the letter(s) of the corresponding region(s).

b. In Calculation B, which two numbers are being multiplied to obtain 0.5? Which numbers are being multiplied to obtain 2.5?

iM KH

## Lesson 7 Summary

Suppose that we want to calculate the product of two numbers that are written in base ten. To explain how, we can use what we know about base-ten numbers and areas of rectangles.

Here is a diagram of a rectangle with side lengths 3.4 units and 1.2 units.

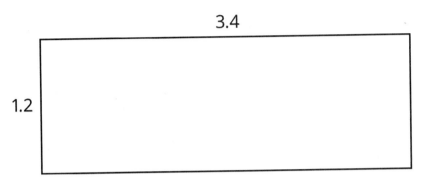

Its area, in square units, is the product

$$(3.4) \cdot (1.2)$$

To calculate this product and find the area of the rectangle, we can decompose each side length into its base-ten units, $3.4 = 3 + 0.4$ and $1.2 = 1 + 0.2$, decomposing the rectangle into four smaller sub-rectangles.

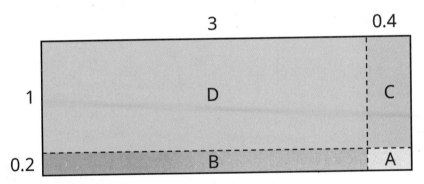

We can rewrite the product and expand it twice:

$$
\begin{aligned}
(3.4) \cdot (1.2) &= (3 + 0.4) \cdot (1 + 0.2) \\
&= (3 + 0.4) \cdot 1 + (3 + 0.4) \cdot 0.2 \\
&= 3 \cdot 1 + 3 \cdot (0.2) + (0.4) \cdot 1 + (0.4) \cdot (0.2)
\end{aligned}
$$

In the last expression, each of the four terms is called a partial product. Each partial product gives the area of a sub-rectangle in the diagram. The sum of the four partial products gives the area of the entire rectangle.

We can show the horizontal calculations above as two vertical calculations.

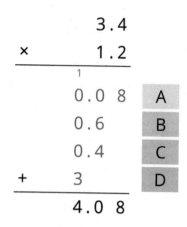

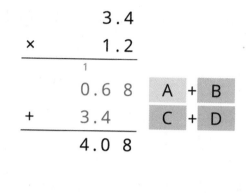

The calculation on the left is an example of the partial products method. It shows the values of each partial product and the letter of the corresponding sub-rectangle. Each partial product gives an area:

- A is 0.2 unit by 0.4 unit, so its area is 0.08 square unit.

- B is 3 units by 0.2 unit, so its area is 0.6 square unit.

- C is 0.4 unit by 1 unit, so its area is 0.4 square unit.

- D is 3 units by 1 unit, so its area is 3 square units.

- The sum of the partial products is $0.08 + 0.6 + 0.4 + 3$, so the area of the rectangle is 4.08 square units.

The calculation on the right shows the values of two products. Each value gives a combined area of two sub-rectangles:

- The combined regions of A and B have an area of 0.68 square units; 0.68 is the value of $(3 + 0.4) \cdot 0.2$.

- The combined regions of C and D have an area of 3.4 square units; 3.4 is the value of $(3 + 0.4) \cdot 1$.

- The sum of the values of two products is $0.68 + 3.4$, so the area of the rectangle is 4.08 square units.

iM KH

# Lesson 7 Practice Problems

1. Here is a rectangle that has been partitioned into four smaller rectangles.

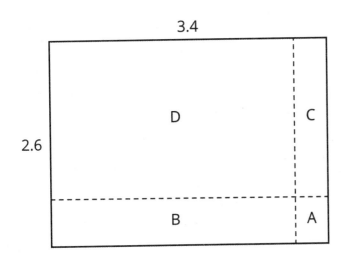

For each expression, choose the sub-rectangle whose area, in square units, matches the expression.

a. $3 \cdot (0.6)$

b. $(0.4) \cdot 2$

c. $(0.4) \cdot (0.6)$

d. $3 \cdot 2$

2. Here is an area diagram that represents $(3.1) \cdot (1.4)$.

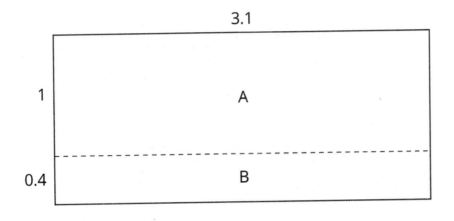

a. Find the areas of sub-rectangles A and B.

b. What is the area of the 3.1 by 1.4 rectangle?

3. Draw an area diagram to find $(0.36) \cdot (0.53)$. Label and organize your work so that it can be followed by others.

4. Find each product. Show your reasoning.

  a. $(2.5) \cdot (1.4)$

  b. $(0.64) \cdot (0.81)$

5. Complete the calculations so that each shows the correct sum.

$$
\begin{array}{r}
2 . 3 \;\square \\
+ \;\square . 6 \; 4 \\
\hline
9 . \square \; 5
\end{array}
\qquad
\begin{array}{r}
2 . 3 \;\square \\
+ \;\square . 6 \; 4 \\
\hline
9 . \square \; 2
\end{array}
$$

$$
\begin{array}{r}
4 . 3 \;\square \\
+ \;\square . 1 \; 5 \\
\hline
6 . \square \; 2
\end{array}
\qquad
\begin{array}{r}
1 . 5 \;\square \\
+ \;\square . 3 \; 8 \\
\hline
1 . \square \; 4
\end{array}
$$

(From Unit 5, Lesson 3.)

6. Diego bought 12 mini muffins for $4.20.

  a. At this rate, how much would Diego pay for 4 mini muffins?

  b. How many mini muffins could Diego buy with $3.00? Explain or show your reasoning. If you get stuck, consider using the table.

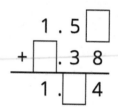

| number of mini muffins | price in dollars |
|---|---|
| 12 | 4.20 |
|  |  |
|  |  |
|  |  |

(From Unit 2, Lesson 12.)

iM KH

# Lesson 8: Calculating Products of Decimals

Let's multiply decimals.

## 8.1: Number Talk: Twenty Times a Number

Evaluate mentally.

$20 \cdot 5$

$20 \cdot (0.8)$

$20 \cdot (0.04)$

$20 \cdot (5.84)$

## 8.2: Calculating Products of Decimals

1. A common way to find a product of decimals is to calculate a product of whole numbers, then place the decimal point in the product.

```
        2 5
  ×     1 2
  ───────────
        5 0
  +   2 5 0
  ───────────
      3 0 0
```

Here is an example for $(2.5) \cdot (1.2)$.

Use what you know about decimals and place value to explain why the decimal point of the product is placed where it is.

$25 \cdot 12 = 300$

$(2.5) \cdot (1.2) = 3.00$

2. Use the method shown in the first question to calculate each product.

   a. $(4.6) \cdot (0.9)$

   b. $(16.5) \cdot (0.7)$

3. Use area diagrams to check your earlier calculations. For each problem:

   ○ Decompose each number into its base-ten units and write them in the boxes on each side of the rectangle.

   ○ Write the area of each lettered region in the diagram. Then find the area of the entire rectangle. Show your reasoning.

   a. $(4.6) \cdot (0.9)$

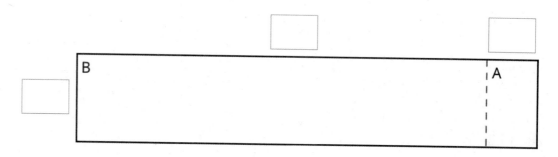

   b. $(16.5) \cdot (0.7)$

4. About how many centimeters are in 6.25 inches if 1 inch is about 2.5 centimeters? Show your reasoning.

iM KH

## 8.3: Practicing Multiplication of Decimals

1. Calculate each product. Show your reasoning. If you get stuck, consider drawing an area diagram to help.

    a. $(5.6) \cdot (1.8)$

    b. $(0.008) \cdot (7.2)$

2. A rectangular playground is 18.2 meters by 12.75 meters.

    a. Find its area in square meters. Show your reasoning.

    b. If 1 meter is approximately 3.28 feet, what are the approximate side lengths of the playground in feet? Show your reasoning.

## Are you ready for more?

1. Write the following expressions as decimals.

   a. $1 - 0.1$

   b. $1 - 0.1 + 10 - 0.01$

   c. $1 - 0.1 + 10 - 0.01 + 100 - 0.001$

2. Describe the decimal that results as this process continues.

3. What would happen to the decimal if all of the addition and subtraction symbols became multiplication symbols? Explain your reasoning.

## Lesson 8 Summary

We can use $84 \cdot 43$ and what we know about place value to find $(8.4) \cdot (4.3)$.

Since 8.4 is 84 tenths and 4.3 is 43 tenths, then:

$$(8.4) \cdot (4.3) = \frac{84}{10} \cdot \frac{43}{10} = \frac{84 \cdot 43}{100}$$

That means we can compute $84 \cdot 43$ and then divide by 100 to find $(8.4) \cdot (4.3)$.

$$84 \cdot 43 = 3612$$
$$(8.4) \cdot (4.3) = 36.12$$

Using fractions such as $\frac{1}{10}$, $\frac{1}{100}$, and $\frac{1}{1,000}$ allows us to find the product of two decimals using the following steps:

- Write each decimal factor as a product of a whole number and a fraction.
- Multiply the whole numbers.
- Multiply the fractions.
- Multiply the products of the whole numbers and fractions.

We know multiplying by fractions such as $\frac{1}{10}$, $\frac{1}{100}$, and $\frac{1}{1,000}$ is the same as dividing by 10, 100, and 1,000, respectively. This means we can move the decimal point in the whole-number product to the left the appropriate number of spaces to correctly place the decimal point.

iM KH

# Lesson 8 Practice Problems

1. Here are an unfinished calculation of (0.54) · (3.8) and a 0.54-by-3.8 rectangle.

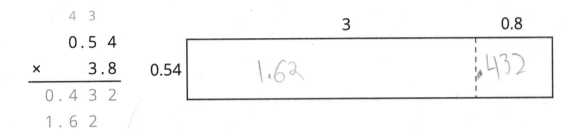

```
  4 3
    0.5 4
  ×     3.8
    0.4 3 2
    1.6 2
```

a. Which part of the rectangle has an area of 0.432? Which part of the rectangle has an area of 1.62? Show your reasoning.

b. What is (0.54) · (3.8)?

2. Explain how the product of 3 and 65 could be used to find (0.03) · (0.65).

3. Use vertical calculation to find each product.

a. (5.4) · (2.4)

b. (1.67) · (3.5)

4. A pound of blueberries costs $3.98 and a pound of clementines costs $2.49. What is the combined cost of 0.6 pound of blueberries and 1.8 pounds of clementines? Round your answer to the nearest cent.

5. Complete the calculations so that each shows the correct sum or difference.

a.

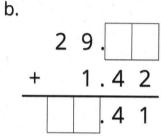

b.

c.

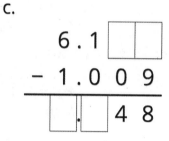

(From Unit 5, Lesson 3.)

6. Which has a greater value: $7.4 - 0.0022$ or $7.39 - 0.0012$? Show your reasoning.

(From Unit 5, Lesson 4.)

7. Andre is planting saplings (baby trees). It takes him 30 minutes to plant 3 saplings. If each sapling takes the same amount of time to plant, how long will it take Andre to plant 14 saplings? If you get stuck, consider using the table.

| number of saplings | time in minutes |
|---|---|
| 3 | 30 |
| 1 | |
| 14 | |

(From Unit 2, Lesson 12.)

iM KH

# Lesson 9: Using the Partial Quotients Method

Let's divide whole numbers.

## 9.1: Using Base-Ten Diagrams to Calculate Quotients

Elena used base-ten diagrams to find 372 ÷ 3. She started by representing 372.

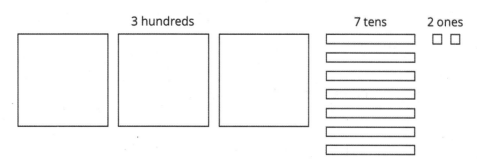

3 hundreds        7 tens    2 ones

She made 3 groups, each with 1 hundred. Then, she put the tens and ones in each of the 3 groups. Here is her diagram for 372 ÷ 3.

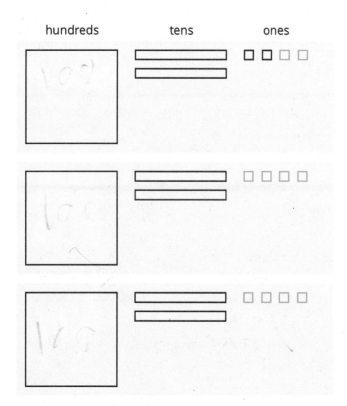

hundreds        tens        ones

Discuss with a partner:

- Elena's diagram for 372 has 7 tens. The one for 372 ÷ 3 has only 6 tens. Why?
- Where did the extra ones (small squares) come from?

# 9.2: Using the Partial Quotients Method to Calculate Quotients

1. Andre calculated $657 \div 3$ using a method that was different from Elena's.

| He started by writing the dividend (657) and the divisor (3). | He then subtracted 3 groups of different amounts from 657, starting with 3 groups of 200 . . . | . . . then 3 groups of 10, and then 3 groups of 9. | Andre calculated 200 + 10 + 9 and then wrote 219. |
|---|---|---|---|
| $3 \overline{)657}$ | $\begin{array}{r} 2\ 0\ 0 \\ 3\overline{)6\ 5\ 7} \\ -\ 6\ 0\ 0 \\ \hline 5\ 7 \end{array}$ | $\begin{array}{r} 9 \\ 1\ 0 \\ 2\ 0\ 0 \\ 3\overline{)6\ 5\ 7} \\ -\ 6\ 0\ 0 \\ \hline 5\ 7 \\ -\ 3\ 0 \\ \hline 2\ 7 \\ -\ 2\ 7 \\ \hline 0 \end{array}$ | $\begin{array}{r} \boxed{2\ 1\ 9} \\ 9 \\ 1\ 0 \\ 2\ 0\ 0 \\ 3\overline{)6\ 5\ 7} \\ -\ 6\ 0\ 0 \\ \hline 5\ 7 \\ -\ 3\ 0 \\ \hline 2\ 7 \\ -\ 2\ 7 \\ \hline 0 \end{array}$ |

a. Andre subtracted 600 from 657. What does the 600 represent?

6 hundred

b. Andre wrote 10 above the 200, and then subtracted 30 from 57. How is the 30 related to the 10?

because they are both tas

c. What do the numbers 200, 10, and 9 represent?

d. What is the meaning of the 0 at the bottom of Andre's work?

2. How might Andre calculate $896 \div 4$? Explain or show your reasoning.

## 9.3: What's the Quotient?

1. Find the quotient of $1,332 \div 9$ using one of the methods you have seen so far. Show your reasoning.

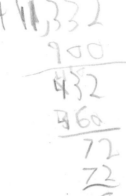

2. Find each quotient and show your reasoning. Use the partial quotients method at least once.

    a. $1,115 \div 5$    223

    b. $665 \div 7$    95

    c. $432 \div 16$    27

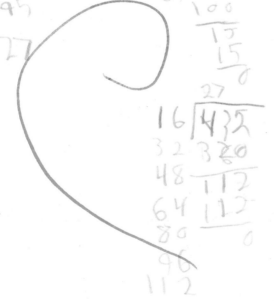

## Lesson 9 Summary

We can find the quotient $345 \div 3$ in different ways.

One way is to use a base-ten diagram to represent the hundreds, tens, and ones and to create equal-sized groups.

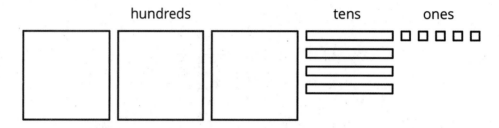

We can think of the division by 3 as splitting up 345 into 3 equal groups.

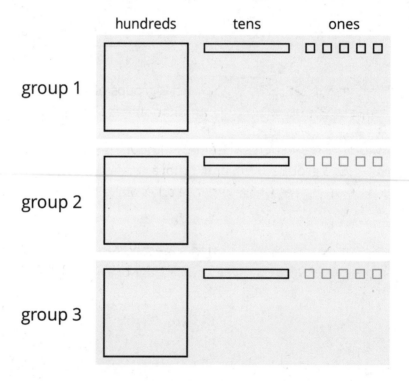

Each group has 1 hundred, 1 ten, and 5 ones, so $345 \div 3 = 115$. Notice that in order to split 345 into 3 equal groups, one of the tens had to be unbundled or decomposed into 10 ones.

iM KH

Another way to divide 345 by 3 is by using the partial quotients method, in which we keep subtracting 3 groups of some amount from 345.

```
     ┌─────────┐                        ┌─────────┐
     │ 1  1  5 │                        │ 1  1  5 │
     └─────────┘                        └─────────┘
            5                                 5  0
         1  0                                 5  0
      1  0  0                                 1  5
    ┌─────────                            ┌─────────
  3 │ 3  4  5                           3 │ 3  4  5
    - 3  0  0  ◄──── 3 groups of 100        -     4  5  ◄──── 3 groups of 15
    ─────────                               ─────────
         4  5                                 3  0  0
    -     3  0  ◄──── 3 groups of 10        - 1  5  0  ◄──── 3 groups of 50
    ─────────                               ─────────
         1  5                                 1  5  0
    -     1  5  ◄──── 3 groups of 5         - 1  5  0  ◄──── 3 groups of 50
    ─────────                               ─────────
            0                                       0
```

- In the calculation on the left, first we subtract 3 groups of 100, then 3 groups of 10, and then 3 groups of 5. Adding up the partial quotients $(100 + 10 + 5)$ gives us 115.

- The calculation on the right shows a different amount per group subtracted each time (3 groups of 15, 3 groups of 50, and 3 more groups of 50), but the total amount in each of the 3 groups is still 115. There are other ways of calculating $345 \div 3$ using the partial quotients method.

Both the base-ten diagrams and partial quotients methods are effective. If, however, the dividend and divisor are large, as in $1,248 \div 26$, then the base-ten diagrams will be time-consuming.

# Lesson 9 Practice Problems

1. Here is one way to find $2,105 \div 5$ using partial quotients. Show a different way of using partial quotients to divide 2,105 by 5.

```
        ┌─────────┐
        │ 4  2  1 │
        └─────────┘
              1
           2  0
        4  0  0
    5 ╱ 2  1  0  5
     -2  0  0  0
    ─────────────
        1  0  5
    -      1  0  0
    ─────────────
              5
    -         5
    ─────────────
              0
```

2. Andre and Jada both found $657 \div 3$ using the partial quotients method, but they did the calculations differently, as shown here.

a. How is Jada's work the same as Andre's work? How is it different?

Andre's Work

```
    ┌─────────┐
    │ 2  1  9 │
    └─────────┘
          9
       1  0
    2  0  0
 3 ╱ 6  5  7
  - 6  0  0
 ───────────
       5  7
    -  3  0
 ───────────
       2  7
    -  2  7
 ───────────
          0
```

Jada's Work

```
    ┌─────────┐
    │ 2  1  9 │
    └─────────┘
          9
       6  0
    1  0  0
       5  0
 3 ╱ 6  5  7
  - 1  5  0
 ───────────
    5  0  7
  - 3  0  0
 ───────────
    2  0  7
  - 1  8  0
 ───────────
       2  7
    -  2  7
 ───────────
          0
```

b. Explain why they have the same answer.

3. Which might be a better way to evaluate $1{,}150 \div 46$: drawing base-ten diagrams or using the partial quotients method? Explain your reasoning.

4. Here is an incomplete calculation of $534 \div 6$.

   Write the missing numbers (marked with "?") that would make the calculation complete.

$$
\begin{array}{r}
\boxed{8\ \ 9} \\
9 \\
8\ \ 0 \\
6\ {\overline{\smash{\big)}\,5\ \ 3\ \ 4\phantom{)}}} \\
-\phantom{xxxx}\ ? \\
\hline
\phantom{xxxx}\ ? \\
-\phantom{xxxx}\ ? \\
\hline
0
\end{array}
$$

5. Use the partial quotients method to find $1{,}032 \div 43$.

6. Which of the polygons has the greatest area?

    A. A rectangle that is 3.25 inches wide and 6.1 inches long.

    B. A square with side length of 4.6 inches.

    C. A parallelogram with a base of 5.875 inches and a height of 3.5 inches.

    D. A triangle with a base of 7.18 inches and a height of 5.4 inches.

(From Unit 5, Lesson 8.)

7. One micrometer is a millionth of a meter. A certain spider web is 4 micrometers thick. A fiber in a shirt is 1 hundred-thousandth of a meter thick.

    a. Which is wider, the spider web or the fiber? Explain your reasoning.

    b. How many meters wider?

(From Unit 5, Lesson 4.)

iM KH

# Lesson 10: Using Long Division

Let's use long division.

## 10.1: Number Talk: Estimating Quotients

Estimate these quotients mentally.

$500 \div 7$

$1{,}394 \div 9$

## 10.2: Lin Uses Long Division

Lin has a method of calculating quotients that is different from Elena's method and Andre's method. Here is how she found the quotient of $657 \div 3$:

| | | | |
|---|---|---|---|
| Lin arranged the numbers for vertical calculations.<br><br>Her plan was to divide each digit of 657 into 3 groups, starting with the 6 hundreds. | There are 3 groups of 2 in 6, so Lin wrote 2 at the top and subtracted 6 from the 6, leaving 0.<br><br>Then, she brought down the 5 tens of 657. | There are 3 groups of 1 in 5, so she wrote 1 at the top and subtracted 3 from 5, which left a remainder of 2. | She brought down the 7 ones of 657 and wrote it next to the 2, which made 27.<br><br>There are 3 groups of 9 in 27, so she wrote 9 at the top and subtracted 27, leaving 0. |

$$3 \overline{)657}$$

$$
\begin{array}{r}
2\phantom{00} \\
3 \overline{)657} \\
-6\phantom{0} \downarrow \\
\hline
0\,5 \\
\end{array}
$$

$$
\begin{array}{r}
2\ 1\phantom{0} \\
3 \overline{)657} \\
-6\phantom{00} \\
\hline
5\phantom{0} \\
-3\phantom{0} \\
\hline
2\phantom{0} \\
\end{array}
$$

$$
\begin{array}{r}
2\ 1\ 9 \\
3 \overline{)657} \\
-6\phantom{000} \\
\hline
5\phantom{00} \\
-3\phantom{0}\downarrow \\
\hline
2\,7 \\
-2\,7 \\
\hline
0 \\
\end{array}
$$

1. Discuss with your partner how Lin's method is similar to and different from drawing base-ten diagrams or using the partial quotients method.

   ○ Lin subtracted $3 \cdot 2$, then $3 \cdot 1$, and lastly $3 \cdot 9$. Earlier, Andre subtracted $3 \cdot 200$, then $3 \cdot 10$, and lastly $3 \cdot 9$. Why did they have the same quotient?

   ○ In the third step, why do you think Lin wrote the 7 next to the remainder of 2 rather than adding 7 and 2 to get 9?

2. Lin's method is called **long division**. Use this method to find the following quotients. Check your answer by multiplying it by the divisor.

   a. $846 \div 3$

   b. $1,816 \div 4$

   c. $768 \div 12$

## 10.3: Dividing Whole Numbers

1. Find each quotient.

   a. $633 \div 3$

   b. $1001 \div 7$

   c. $2996 \div 14$

iM KH

2. Here is Priya's calculation of $906 \div 3$.

```
      3 2 0
3 / 9 0 6
  - 9
  _____
        0 6
  -       6
  _____
          0
```

a. Priya wrote 320 for the value of $906 \div 3$. Check her answer by multiplying it by 3. What product do you get and what does it tell you about Priya's answer?

b. Describe Priya's mistake, then show the correct calculation and answer.

## Lesson 10 Summary

**Long division** is another method for calculating quotients. It relies on place value to perform and record the division.

When we use long division, we work from left to right and with one digit at a time, starting with the leftmost digit of the dividend. We remove the largest group possible each time, using the placement of the digit to indicate the size of each group. Here is an example of how to find $948 \div 3$ using long division.

```
      3 1 6
3 / 9 4 8
  - 9              ◄——— 3 groups of 3 (hundreds)
  _____
        4
  -     3          ◄——— 3 groups of 1 (ten)
  _____
        1 8
  -     1 8        ◄——— 3 groups of 6 (ones)
  _____
          0
```

- We start by dividing 9 hundreds into 3 groups, which means 3 hundreds in each group. Instead of writing 300, we simply write 3 in the hundreds place, knowing that it means 3 hundreds.

- There are no remaining hundreds, so we work with the tens. We can make 3 groups of 1 ten in 4 tens, so we write 1 in the tens place above the 4 of 948. Subtracting 3 tens from 4 tens, we have a remainder of 1 ten.

- We know that 1 ten is 10 ones. Combining these with the 8 ones from 948, we have 18 ones. We can make 3 groups of 6, so we write 6 in the ones place.

In total, there are 3 groups of 3 hundreds, 1 ten, and 6 ones in 948, so $948 \div 3 = 316$.

## Glossary

- long division

# Lesson 10 Practice Problems

1. Kiran is using long division to find $696 \div 12$.

$$12 \overline{)696}$$

He starts by dividing 69 by 12. In which decimal place should Kiran place the first digit of the quotient (5)?

A. Hundreds

B. Tens

C. Ones

D. Tenths

2. Here is a long-division calculation of $917 \div 7$.

```
      1 3 1
   7 )9 1 7
     - 7
      2 1
     - 2 1
         7
       - 7
         0
```

a. There is a 7 under the 9 of 917. What does this 7 represent?

b. What does the subtraction of 7 from 9 mean?

c. Why is a 1 written next to the 2 from $9 - 7$?

3. Han's calculation of $972 \div 9$ is shown here.

```
      1 8 0
   9 )9 7 2
     - 9
       7 2
     - 7 2
         0
       - 0
         0
```

a. Find $180 \cdot 9$.

b. Use your calculation of $180 \cdot 9$ to explain how you know Han has made a mistake.

c. Identify and correct Han's mistake.

iM KH

4. Find each quotient.

a.

$$5\overline{)465}$$

b.

$$12\overline{)924}$$

c.

$$3\overline{)1107}$$

5. One ounce of a yogurt contains of 1.2 grams of sugar. How many grams of sugar are in 14.25 ounces of yogurt?

A. 0.171 grams

B. 1.71 grams

C. 17.1 grams

D. 171 grams

(From Unit 5, Lesson 7.)

6. The mass of one coin is 16.718 grams. The mass of a second coin is 27.22 grams. How much greater is the mass of the second coin than the first? Show your reasoning.

(From Unit 5, Lesson 4.)

# Lesson 11: Dividing Numbers that Result in Decimals

Let's find quotients that are not whole numbers.

## 11.1: Number Talk: Evaluating Quotients

Find the quotients mentally.

$400 \div 8$   50

$80 \div 8$   10

$16 \div 8$   2

$496 \div 8$   62

## 11.2: Keep Dividing

Mai used base-ten diagrams to calculate $62 \div 5$. She started by representing 62.

6 tens     2 ones

12.4

She then made 5 groups, each with 1 ten. There was 1 ten left. She unbundled it into 10 ones and distributed the ones across the 5 groups.

iM KH

Here is Mai's diagram for $62 \div 5$.

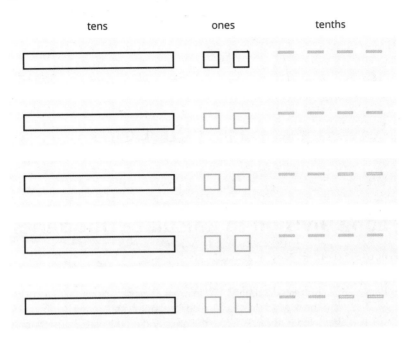

1. Discuss these questions with a partner and write down your answers:

   a. Mai should have a total of 12 ones, but her diagram shows only 10. Why?

   b. She did not originally have tenths, but in her diagram each group has 4 tenths. Why?

   c. What value has Mai found for $62 \div 5$? Explain your reasoning.

2. Find the quotient of $511 \div 5$ by drawing base-ten diagrams or by using the partial quotients method. Show your reasoning. If you get stuck, work with your partner to find a solution.

3. Four students share a $271 prize from a science competition. How much does each student get if the prize is shared equally? Show your reasoning.

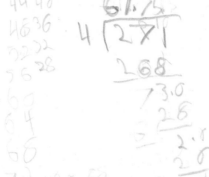

## 11.3: Using Long Division to Calculate Quotients

Here is how Lin calculated $62 \div 5$.

| Lin set up the numbers for long division. | She subtracted 5 times 1 from the 6, which leaves a remainder of 1. | Lin drew a vertical line and a decimal point, separating the ones and tenths place. | Lastly, she subtracted 5 times 4 from 20, which left no remainder. |
|---|---|---|---|
| | She wrote the 2 from 62 next to the 1, which made 12, and subtracted 5 times 2 from 12. | 12 – 10 is 2. She wrote 0 to the right of the 2, which made 20. | At the top, she wrote 4 next to the decimal point. |

```
                    1                 1 2.             1 2. 4
  5 ) 6 2       5 ) 6 2           5 ) 6 2.          5 ) 6 2.
                  - 5               - 5               - 5
                  ----              ----              ----
                  1 2               1 2.              1 2.
                - 1 0             - 1 0             - 1 0
                  ----              ----              ----
                    2               2. 0              2. 0
                                                    - 2. 0
                                                      ----
                                                        0
```

1. Discuss with your partner:

   ○ Lin put a 0 after the remainder of 2. Why? Why does this 0 not change the value of the quotient?

   ○ Lin subtracted 5 groups of 4 from 20. What value does the 4 in the quotient represent?

   ○ What value did Lin find for $62 \div 5$?

iM KH

2. Use long division to find the value of each expression. Then pause so your teacher can review your work.

a. $126 \div 8$

b. $90 \div 12$

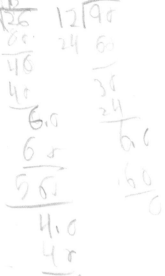

3. Use long division to show that:

a. $5 \div 4$, or $\frac{5}{4}$, is 1.25.

b. $4 \div 5$, or $\frac{4}{5}$, is 0.8.

c. $1 \div 8$, or $\frac{1}{8}$, is 0.125.

d. $1 \div 25$, or $\frac{1}{25}$, is 0.04.

4. Noah said we cannot use long division to calculate $10 \div 3$ because there will always be a remainder.

a. What do you think Noah meant by "there will always be a remainder"?

b. Do you agree with him? Explain your reasoning.

## Lesson 11 Summary

Dividing a whole number by another whole number does not always produce a whole-number quotient. Let's look at $86 \div 4$, which we can think of as dividing 86 into 4 equal groups.

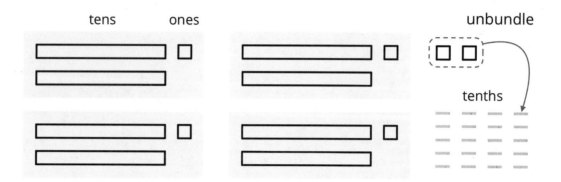

We can see in the base-ten diagram that there are 4 groups of 21 in 86 with 2 ones left over. To find the quotient, we need to distribute the 2 ones into the 4 groups. To do this, we can unbundle or decompose the 2 ones into 20 tenths, which enables us to put 5 tenths in each group.

Once the 20 tenths are distributed, each group will have 2 tens, 1 one, and 5 tenths, so $86 \div 4 = 21.5$.

We can also calculate $86 \div 4$ using long division.

The calculation shows that, after removing 4 groups of 21, there are 2 ones remaining. We can continue dividing by writing a 0 to the right of the 2 and thinking of that remainder as 20 tenths, which can then be divided into 4 groups.

```
       2 1 . 5
   4 / 8 6
     - 8
     ─────
         6
       - 4
       ─────
         2 0
       - 2 0
       ─────
           0
```

To show that the quotient we are working with now is in the tenth place, we put a decimal point to the right of the 1 (which is in the ones place) at the top. It may also be helpful to draw a vertical line to separate the ones and the tenths.

There are 4 groups of 5 tenths in 20 tenths, so we write 5 in the tenths place at the top. The calculation likewise shows $86 \div 4 = 21.5$.

iM KH

# Lesson 11 Practice Problems

1. Use long division to show that the fraction and decimal in each pair are equal.

    $\frac{3}{4}$ and 0.75                $\frac{3}{50}$ and 0.06                $\frac{7}{25}$ and 0.28

2. Mai walked $\frac{1}{8}$ of a 30-mile walking trail. How many miles did Mai walk? Explain or show your reasoning.

3. Use long division to find each quotient. Write your answer as a decimal.

    a. $99 \div 12$

    b. $216 \div 5$

    c. $1,988 \div 8$

4. Tyler reasoned: "$\frac{9}{25}$ is equivalent to $\frac{18}{50}$ and to $\frac{36}{100}$, so the decimal of $\frac{9}{25}$ is 0.36."

    a. Use long division to show that Tyler is correct.

    b. Is the decimal of $\frac{18}{50}$ also 0.36? Use long division to support your answer.

5. Complete the calculations so that each shows the correct difference.

    a.

$$5$$
$$- \boxed{\phantom{0}\,|\,\phantom{0}\,|\,\phantom{0}\,|\,\phantom{0}}$$
$$4 . 3 \ 2 \ 9$$

    b.

$$1$$
$$- \boxed{\phantom{0}\,|\,\phantom{0}\,|\,\phantom{0}\,|\,\phantom{0}}$$
$$0 . 0 \ 1 \ 5$$

    c.

$$1$$
$$- \boxed{\phantom{0}\,|\,\phantom{0}\,|\,\phantom{0}\,|\,\phantom{0}}$$
$$0 . 8 \ 6 \ 3$$

(From Unit 5, Lesson 4.)

6. Use the equation $124 \cdot 15 = 1{,}860$ and what you know about fractions, decimals, and place value to explain how to place the decimal point when you compute $(1.24) \cdot (0.15)$.

(From Unit 5, Lesson 6.)

iM KH

# Lesson 12: Dividing Decimals by Whole Numbers

Let's divide decimals by whole numbers.

## 12.1: Number Talk: Dividing by 4

Find each quotient mentally.

$80 \div 4$

$12 \div 4$

$1.2 \div 4$

$81.2 \div 4$

## 12.2: Using Diagrams to Represent Division

To find $53.8 \div 4$ using diagrams, Elena began by representing 53.8.

|  | 5 tens | 3 ones | 8 tenths |
|---|---|---|---|

She placed 1 ten into each group, unbundled the remaining 1 ten into 10 ones, and went on distributing the units.

This diagram shows Elena's initial placement of the units and the unbundling of 1 ten.

| | tens | ones | tenths | hundredths |
|---|---|---|---|---|
| group 1 | ▭ | ☐ | ≡ | |
| group 2 | ▭ | ☐ | ≡ | |
| group 3 | ▭ | ☐ | ≡ | |
| group 4 | ▭ | | ≡ | |

▭ unbundle → ☐ ☐ ☐ ☐ ☐
☐ ☐ ☐ ☐ ☐

1. Complete the diagram by continuing the division process. How would you use the available units to make 4 equal groups?

   As the units get placed into groups, show them accordingly and cross out those pieces from the bottom. If you unbundle a unit, draw the resulting pieces.

2. What value did you find for 53.8 ÷ 4? Be prepared to explain your reasoning.

3. Use long division to find 53.8 ÷ 4. Check your answer by multiplying it by the divisor 4.

4. Use long division to find 77.4 ÷ 5. If you get stuck, you can draw diagrams or use another method.

   15.48

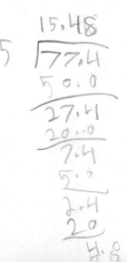

iM KH

**Are you ready for more?**

A distant, magical land uses jewels for their bartering system. The jewels are valued and ranked in order of their rarity. Each jewel is worth 3 times the jewel immediately below it in the ranking. The ranking is red, orange, yellow, green, blue, indigo, and violet. So a red jewel is worth 3 orange jewels, a green jewel is worth 3 blue jewels, and so on.

A group of 4 craftsmen are paid 1 of each jewel. If they split the jewels evenly amongst themselves, which jewels does each craftsman get?

## 12.3: Dividends and Divisors

Analyze the dividends, divisors, and quotients in the calculations, and then answer the questions.

```
      2 4            2 4              2 4                 2 4
 3 / 7 2        30 / 7 2 0      300 / 7 2 0 0      3000 / 7 2 0 0 0
   - 6            - 6 0            - 6 0 0            - 6 0 0 0
   ----           -----           -------           ---------
   1 2            1 2 0            1 2 0 0            1 2 0 0 0
  - 1 2          - 1 2 0          - 1 2 0 0          - 1 2 0 0 0
  -----          -------          ---------          -----------
     0              0                0                   0
```

1. Complete each sentence. In the calculations shown:

   ○ Each dividend is _____ times the dividend to the left of it.

   ○ Each divisor is _____ times the divisor to the left of it.

   ○ Each quotient is _____ the quotient to the left of it.

2. Suppose we are writing a calculation to the right of $72,000 \div 3,000$. Which expression has a quotient of 24? Be prepared to explain your reasoning.

   a. $72,000 \div 30,000$

   b. $720,000 \div 300,000$

   c. $720,000 \div 30,000$

   d. $720,000 \div 3,000$

3. Suppose we are writing a calculation to the left of $72 \div 3$. Write an expression that would also give a quotient of 24. Be prepared to explain your reasoning.

4. Decide which of the following expressions would have the same value as $250 \div 10$. Be prepared to share your reasoning.

   a. $250 \div 0.1$

   b. $25 \div 1$

   c. $2.5 \div 1$

   d. $2.5 \div 0.1$

   e. $2,500 \div 100$

   f. $0.25 \div 0.01$

## Lesson 12 Summary

We know that fractions such as $\frac{6}{4}$ and $\frac{60}{40}$ are equivalent because:

- The numerator and denominator of $\frac{60}{40}$ are each 10 times those of $\frac{6}{4}$.
- Both fractions can be simplified to $\frac{3}{2}$.
- 600 divided by 400 is 1.5, and 60 divided by 40 is also 1.5.

Just like fractions, division expressions can be equivalent. For example, the expressions $540 \div 90$ and $5,400 \div 900$ are both equivalent to $54 \div 9$ because:

- They all have a quotient of 6.
- The dividend and the divisor in $540 \div 90$ are each 10 times the dividend and divisor in $54 \div 9$. Those in $5,400 \div 900$ are each 100 times the dividend and divisor in $54 \div 9$. In both cases, the quotient does not change.

This means that an expression such as $5.4 \div 0.9$ also has the same value as $54 \div 9$. Both the dividend and divisor of $5.4 \div 0.9$ are $\frac{1}{10}$ of those in $54 \div 9$.

In general, multiplying a dividend and a divisor by the same number does not change the quotient. Multiplying by powers of 10 (e.g., 10, 100, 1,000, etc.) can be particularly useful for dividing decimals, as we will see in an upcoming lesson.

iM KH

# Lesson 12 Practice Problems

1. Here is a diagram representing a base-ten number. The large rectangle represents a unit that is 10 times the value of the square. The square represents a unit that is 10 times the value of the small rectangle.

Here is a diagram showing the number being divided into 5 equal groups.

a. If a large rectangle represents 1,000, what division problem did the second diagram show? What is its answer?

b. If a large rectangle represents 100, what division problem did the second diagram show? What is its answer?

c. If a large rectangle represents 10, what division problem did the second diagram show? What is its answer?

2. a. Explain why all of these expressions have the same value.

$$4.5 \div 0.09 \qquad 45 \div 0.9 \qquad 450 \div 9 \qquad 4500 \div 90$$

b. What is the common value?

3. Use long division to find each quotient.

a. $7.89 \div 2$

$$3.945$$

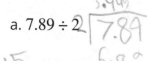

```
  3.945
2)7.89
  6.00
  1.89
  18.0
    9
    8
   1.0
   1.0
    0
```

a. $39.54 \div 3$

```
   13.18
3)39.54
  30.00
   9.54
   9.00
    .54
    30
    24
    24
     0
```

$13.18$

a. $0.176 \div 5$

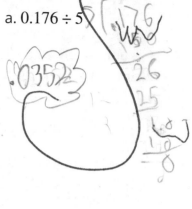

$.0352$

```
   .0352
5)176
   150
    26
    25
    1.0
    1.0
     0
```

4. Four students set up a lemonade stand. At the end of the day, their profit is $17.52. How much money do they each have when the profit is split equally? Show or explain your reasoning.

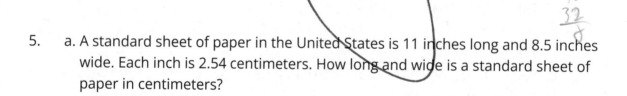

$4.38$

```
   4.38
4)17.52
  16.00
   1.52
   1.2
    32
    32
     0
```

5.    a. A standard sheet of paper in the United States is 11 inches long and 8.5 inches wide. Each inch is 2.54 centimeters. How long and wide is a standard sheet of paper in centimeters?

b. A standard sheet of paper in Europe is 21.0 cm wide and 29.7 cm long. Which has the greater area, the standard sheet of paper in the United States or the standard sheet of paper in Europe? Explain your reasoning.

(From Unit 5, Lesson 8.)

iM KH

# Lesson 13: Dividing Decimals by Decimals

Let's divide decimals by decimals.

## 13.1: Same Values

1. Use long division to find the value of $5.04 \div 7$.

2. Select **all** of the quotients that have the same value as $5.04 \div 7$. Be prepared to explain how you know.

   a. $5.04 \div 70$

   b. $50.4 \div 70$

   c. $504{,}000 \div 700$

   d. $504{,}000 \div 700{,}000$

## 13.2: Placing Decimal Points in Quotients

1. Think of one or more ways to find $3 \div 0.12$. Show your reasoning.

2. Find $1.8 \div 0.004$. Show your reasoning. If you get stuck, think about what equivalent division expression you could write.

3. Diego said, "To divide decimals, we can start by moving the decimal point in both the dividend and divisor by the same number of places and in the same direction. Then we find the quotient of the resulting numbers."

   Do you agree with Diego? Use the division expression $7.5 \div 1.25$ to support your answer.

**Are you ready for more?**

Can we create an equivalent division expression by multiplying both the dividend and divisor by a number that is *not* a multiple of 10 (for example: 4, 20, or $\frac{1}{2}$)? Would doing so produce the same quotient? Explain or show your reasoning.

## 13.3: Two Ways to Calculate Quotients of Decimals

1. Here are two calculations of $48.78 \div 9$. Work with your partner to answer the following questions.

```
           5. 4 2                              5. 4 2
   9 / 4 8. 7 8               9 0 0 / 4 8 7 8
     - 4 5                            - 4 5 0 0
         3  7                              3 7 8  0
       - 3  6                            - 3 6 0  0
            1  8                              1 8  0 0
          -  1  8                          -  1 8  0 0
               0                                    0
```

        Calculation A                 Calculation B

   a. How are the two calculations the same? How are they different?

   b. Look at Calculation A. Explain how you can tell that the 36 means "36 tenths" and the 18 means "18 hundredths."

   c. Look at Calculation B. What do the 3600 and 1800 mean?

d. We can think of $48.78 \div 9 = 5.42$ as saying, "There are 9 groups of 5.42 in 48.78." We can think of $4878 \div 900 = 5.42$ as saying, "There are 900 groups of 5.42 in 4878." How might we show that both statements are true?

2.  a. Explain why $51.2 \div 6.4$ has the same value as $5.12 \div 0.64$.

    b. Write a division expression that has the same value as $51.2 \div 6.4$ but is easier to use to find the value. Then, find the value using long division.

## 13.4: Practicing Division with Decimals

Find each quotient. Discuss your quotients with your group and agree on the correct answers. Consult your teacher if the group can't agree.

1. $106.5 \div 3$

2. $58.8 \div 0.7$

3. $257.4 \div 1.1$

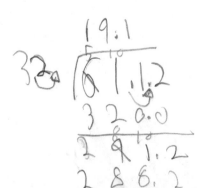

4. Mai is making friendship bracelets. Each bracelet is made from 24.3 cm of string. If she has 170.1 cm of string, how many bracelets can she make? Explain or show your reasoning.

## Lesson 13 Summary

One way to find a quotient of two decimals is to multiply each decimal by a power of 10 so that both products are whole numbers.

If we multiply both decimals by the same power of 10, this does not change the value of the quotient. For example, the quotient $7.65 \div 1.2$ can be found by multiplying the two decimals by 10 (or by 100) and instead finding $76.5 \div 12$ or $765 \div 120$.

To calculate $765 \div 120$, which is equivalent to $76.5 \div 12$, we could use base-ten diagrams, partial quotients, or long division. Here is the calculation with long division:

```
              6 . 3 7 5
        _____
120 /  7 6 5
     - 7 2 0
     _____
         4 5 0
       - 3 6 0
       _____
           9 0 0
         - 8 4 0
         _____
             6 0 0
           - 6 0 0
           _____
                 0
```

# Lesson 13 Practice Problems

1. A student said, "To find the value of $109.2 \div 6$, I can divide 1,092 by 60."

   a. Do you agree with her? Explain your reasoning.

   b. Calculate the quotient of $109.2 \div 6$ using any method of your choice.

2. Here is how Han found $31.59 \div 13$:

```
        2 . 4 3
  13 / 3 1 . 5 9
     - 2 6
       5 5
     - 5 2
         3 9
       - 3 9
           0
```

   a. At the second step, Han subtracts 52 from 55. How do you know that these numbers represent tenths?

   b. At the third step, Han subtracts 39 from 39. How do you know that these numbers represent hundredths?

   c. Check that Han's answer is correct by calculating the product of 2.43 and 13.

3.  a. Write two division expressions that have the same value as $61.12 \div 3.2$.

    b. Find the value of $61.12 \div 3.2$. Show your reasoning.

4. A bag of pennies weighs 5.1 kilograms. Each penny weighs 2.5 grams. About how many pennies are in the bag?

    A. 20

    B. 200

    C. 2,000

    D. 20,000

5. Find each difference. If you get stuck, consider drawing a diagram.

$2.5 - 1.6$ $\qquad$ $0.72 - 0.4$ $\qquad$ $11.3 - 1.75$ $\qquad$ $73 - 1.3$

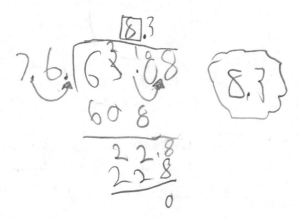

(From Unit 5, Lesson 3.)

iM KH

6. Plant B is $6\frac{2}{3}$ inches tall. Plant C is $4\frac{4}{15}$ inches tall. Complete the sentences and show your reasoning.

   a. Plant C is _____ times as tall as Plant B.

   b. Plant C is _____ inches _____ (taller or shorter) than Plant B.

(From Unit 4, Lesson 12.)

7. At a school, 460 of the students walk to school.

   a. The number of students who take public transit is 20% of the number of students who walk. How many students take public transit?

   b. The number of students who bike to school is 5% of the number of students who walk. How many students bike to school?

   c. The number of students who ride the school bus is 110% of the number of students who walk. How many students ride the school bus?

(From Unit 3, Lesson 15.)

# Lesson 14: Using Operations on Decimals to Solve Problems

Let's solve some problems using decimals.

## 14.1: Close Estimates

For each expression, choose the best estimate of its value.

1. $76.2 \div 15$

   - ○ 0.5
   - ● 5
   - ○ 50

2. $56.34 \div 48$

   - ● 1
   - ○ 10
   - ○ 100

3. $124.3 \div 20$

   - ● 6
   - ○ 60
   - ○ 600

iM KH

# 14.2: Applying Division with Decimals

Your teacher will assign to you either Problem A or Problem B. Work together as a group to answer the questions. Be prepared to create a visual display to show your reasoning with the class.

Problem A:

A piece of rope is 5.75 meters in length.

    1. If it is cut into 20 equal pieces, how long will each piece be?

    2. If it is cut into 0.05-meter pieces, how many pieces will there be?

Problem B:

A tortoise travels 0.945 miles in 3.5 hours.

    1. If it moves at a constant speed, how many miles per hour is it traveling?

    2. At this rate, how long will it take the tortoise to travel 4.86 miles?

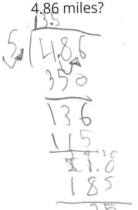

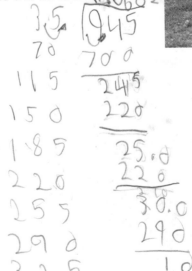

## 14.3: Distance between Hurdles

There are 10 equally-spaced hurdles on a race track.
The first hurdle is 13.72 meters from the start line.
The final hurdle is 14.02 meters from the finish line.
The race track is 110 meters long.

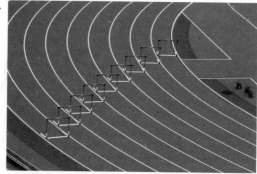

1. Draw a diagram that shows the hurdles on the race track. Label all known measurements.

2. How far are the hurdles from one another? Explain or show your reasoning.

3. A professional runner takes 3 strides between each pair of hurdles. The runner leaves the ground 2.2 meters *before* the hurdle and returns to the ground 1 meter *after* the hurdle.

   About how long are each of the runner's strides between the hurdles? Show your reasoning.

iM KH

# 14.4: Examining a Tennis Court

Here is a diagram of a tennis court.

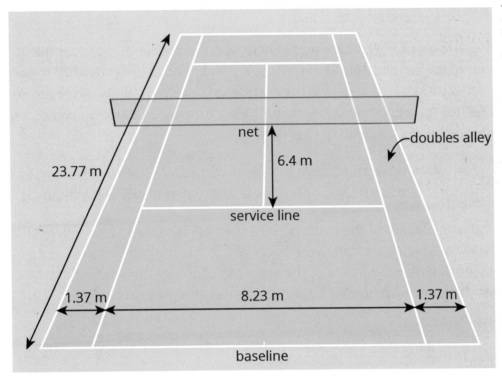

The full tennis court, used for doubles, is a rectangle. All of the angles made by the line segments in the diagram are right angles.

1. The net partitions the tennis court into two halves. Is each half a square? Explain your reasoning.

2. Is the service line halfway between the net and the baseline? Explain your reasoning.

3. Lines painted on a tennis court are 5 cm wide. A painter made markings to show the length and width of the court, then painted the lines to the outside of the markings.

   a. Did the painter's mistake increase or decrease the overall size of the tennis court? Explain how you know.

   b. By how many square meters did the court's size change? Explain your reasoning.

## Lesson 14 Summary

Diagrams can help us communicate and model mathematics. A clearly-labeled diagram helps us visualize what is happening in a problem and accurately communicate the information we need.

Sports offer great examples of how diagrams can help us solve problems. For example, to show the placement of the running hurdles in a diagram, we needed to know what the distances 13.72 and 14.02 meters tell us and the number of hurdles to draw. An accurate diagram not only helped us set up and solve the problem correctly, but also helped us see that there are only *nine* spaces between ten hurdles.

To communicate information clearly and solve problems correctly, it is also important to be precise in our measurements and calculations, especially when they involve decimals.

In tennis, for example, the length of the court is 23.77 meters. Because the boundary lines on a tennis court have a significant width, we would want to know whether this measurement is taken between the inside of the lines, the center of the lines, or the outside of the lines. Diagrams can help us attend to this detail, as shown here.

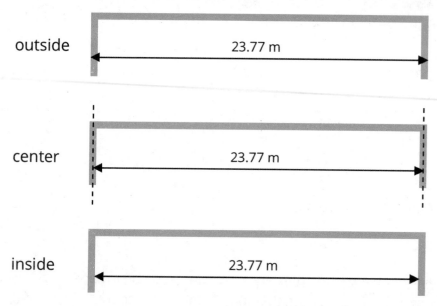

The accuracy of this measurement matters to the tennis players who use the court, so it matters to those who paint the boundaries as well. The tennis players practice their shots to be on or within certain lines. If the tennis court on which they play is not precisely measured, their shots may not land as intended in relation to the boundaries. Court painters usually need to be sure their measurements are accurate to within $\frac{1}{100}$ of a meter or one centimeter.

iM KH

# Lesson 14 Practice Problems

1. A roll of ribbon was 12 meters long. Diego cut 9 pieces of ribbon that were 0.4 meter each to tie some presents. He then used the remaining ribbon to make some wreaths. Each wreath required 0.6 meter. For each question, explain your reasoning.

    a. How many meters of ribbon were available for making wreaths?

    b. How many wreaths could Diego make with the available ribbon?

2. The Amazon rainforest covered 6.42 million square kilometers in 1994. In 2014, it covered only $\frac{50}{59}$ as much. Which is closest to the area of the Amazon forest in 2014? Explain how you know without calculating the exact area.

    A. 6.4 million $km^2$

    B. 5.4 million $km^2$

    C. 4.4 million $km^2$

    D. 3.4 million $km^2$

    E. 2.4 million $km^2$

3. To get an A in her math class, Jada needs to have at least 90% of the total number of points possible. The table shows Jada's results before the final test in the class.

| | Jada's points | total points possible |
|---|---|---|
| Homework | 141 | 150 |
| Test 1 | 87 | 100 |
| Test 2 | 81 | 100 |
| Test 3 | 91 | 100 |

a. Does Jada have 90% of the total possible points *before* the final test? Explain how you know.

b. Jada thinks that if she gets at least 92 out of 100 on the final test, she will get an A in the class. Do you agree? Explain.

4. Find the following differences. Show your reasoning.

   ○ $0.151 - 0.028$      ○ $0.106 - 0.0315$      ○ $3.572 - 2.6014$

(From Unit 5, Lesson 4.)

5. Find these quotients. Show your reasoning.

   ○ $24.2 \div 1.1$      ○ $13.25 \div 0.4$      ○ $170.28 \div 0.08$

(From Unit 5, Lesson 13.)

iM KH

# Lesson 15: Making and Measuring Boxes

Let's use what we know about decimals to make and measure boxes.

## 15.1: Folding Paper Boxes

Your teacher will demonstrate how to make an open-top box by folding a sheet of paper. Your group will receive 3 or more sheets of square paper. Each person in your group will make 1 box. Before you begin folding:

1. Record the side lengths of your papers, from the smallest to the largest.

    ○ Paper for Box 1: _____ cm

    ○ Paper for Box 2: _____ cm

    ○ Paper for Box 3: _____ cm

2. Compare the side lengths of the square sheets of paper. Be prepared to explain how you know.

    a. The side length of the paper for Box 2 is _____ times the side length of the paper for Box 1.

    b. The side length of the paper for Box 3 is _____ times the side length of the paper for Box 1.

3. Make some predictions about the measurements of the three boxes your group will make:

    ○ The surface area of Box 3 will be _____ as large as that of Box 1.

    ○ Box 2 will be _____ times as tall as Box 1.

    ○ Box 3 will be _____ times as tall as Box 1.

Now you are ready to fold your paper into a box!

# 15.2: Sizing Up Paper Boxes

Now that you have made your boxes, you will measure them and check your predictions about how their heights and surface areas compare.

1. a. Measure the length and height of each box to the nearest tenth of a centimeter. Record the measurements in the table.

|  | side length of paper (cm) | length of box (cm) | height of box (cm) | surface area (sq cm) |
|---|---|---|---|---|
| Box 1 |  |  |  |  |
| Box 2 |  |  |  |  |
| Box 3 |  |  |  |  |

b. Calculate the surface area of each box. Show your reasoning and decide on an appropriate level of precision for describing the surface area (Is it the nearest 10 square centimeters, nearest square centimeter, or something else?). Record your answers in the table.

iM KH

2. To see how many times as large one measurement is when compared to another, we can compute their quotient. Divide each measurement of Box 2 by the corresponding measurement for Box 1 to complete the following statements.

    a. The length of Box 2 is _____ times the length of Box 1.

    b. The height of Box 2 is _____ times the height of Box 1.

    c. The surface area of Box 2 is _____ times the surface area of Box 1.

3. Find out how the dimensions of Box 3 compare to those of Box 1 by computing quotients of their lengths, heights, and surface areas. Show your reasoning.

    a. The length of Box 3 is _____ times the length of Box 1.

    b. The height of Box 3 is _____ times the height of Box 1.

    c. The surface area of Box 3 is _____ times the surface area of Box 1.

4. Record your results in the table.

|  | side length of paper | length of box | height of box | surface area |
|---|---|---|---|---|
| Box 2 compared to Box 1 |  |  |  |  |
| Box 3 compared to Box 1 |  |  |  |  |

5. Earlier, in the first activity, you made predictions about how the heights and surface areas of the two larger boxes would compare to those of the smallest box. Discuss with your group:

  ○ How accurate were your predictions? Were they close to the results you found by performing calculations?

  ○ Let's say you had another piece of square paper to make Box 4. If the side length of this paper is 4 times the side length of the paper for Box 1, predict how the length, height, and surface area of Box 4 would compare to those of Box 1. How did you make your prediction?

iM KH

# Learning Targets

**Lesson 1: Using Decimals in a Shopping Context**

- I can use decimals to make estimates and calculations about money.

**Lesson 2: Using Diagrams to Represent Addition and Subtraction**

- I can use diagrams to represent and reason about addition and subtraction of decimals.

- I can use place value to explain addition and subtraction of decimals.

- I can use vertical calculations to represent and reason about addition and subtraction of decimals.

**Lesson 3: Adding and Subtracting Decimals with Few Non-Zero Digits**

- I can tell whether writing or removing a zero in a decimal will change its value.

- I know how to solve subtraction problems with decimals that require "unbundling" or "decomposing."

**Lesson 4: Adding and Subtracting Decimals with Many Non-Zero Digits**

- I can solve problems that involve addition and subtraction of decimals.

**Lesson 5: Decimal Points in Products**

- I can use place value and fractions to reason about multiplication of decimals.

**Lesson 6: Methods for Multiplying Decimals**

- I can use area diagrams to represent and reason about multiplication of decimals.

- I know and can explain more than one way to multiply decimals using fractions and place value.

**Lesson 7: Using Diagrams to Represent Multiplication**

- I can use area diagrams and partial products to represent and find products of decimals.

### Lesson 8: Calculating Products of Decimals

- I can describe and apply a method for multiplying decimals.

- I know how to use a product of whole numbers to find a product of decimals.

### Lesson 9: Using the Partial Quotients Method

- I can use the partial quotients method to find a quotient of two whole numbers when the quotient is a whole number.

### Lesson 10: Using Long Division

- I can use long division to find a quotient of two whole numbers when the quotient is a whole number.

### Lesson 11: Dividing Numbers that Result in Decimals

- I can use long division to find the quotient of two whole numbers when the quotient is not a whole number.

### Lesson 12: Dividing Decimals by Whole Numbers

- I can divide a decimal by a whole number.

- I can explain the division of a decimal by a whole number in terms of equal-sized groups.

- I know how multiplying both the dividend and the divisor by the same factor affects the quotient.

### Lesson 13: Dividing Decimals by Decimals

- I can explain how multiplying dividend and divisor by the same power of 10 can help me find a quotient of two decimals.

- I can find the quotient of two decimals.

### Lesson 14: Using Operations on Decimals to Solve Problems

- I can use addition, subtraction, multiplication, and division on decimals to solve problems.

### Lesson 15: Making and Measuring Boxes

- I can use the four operations on decimals to find surface areas and reason about real-world problems.

# GRADE 6

Unit

# 6

STUDENT EDITION
Book 2

# Kendall Hunt |

# Lesson 1: Tape Diagrams and Equations

Let's see how tape diagrams and equations can show relationships between amounts.

## 1.1: Which Diagram is Which?

1. Here are two diagrams. One represents $2 + 5 = 7$. The other represents $5 \cdot 2 = 10$. Which is which? Label the length of each diagram.

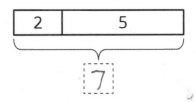

| 2 | 2 | 2 | 2 | 2 |
|---|---|---|---|---|

10

| 2 | 5 |
|---|---|

7

2. Draw a diagram that represents each equation.

$$4 + 3 = 7 \qquad\qquad 4 \cdot 3 = 12$$

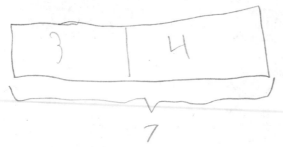

## 1.2: Match Equations and Tape Diagrams

Here are two tape diagrams. Match each equation to one of the tape diagrams.

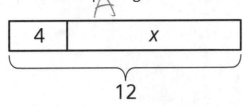

A

| 4 | x |
|---|---|

12

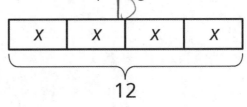

B

| x | x | x | x |
|---|---|---|---|

12

- $4 + x = 12$ A
- $12 \div 4 = x$ B
- $4 \cdot x = 12$ B

- $12 = 4 + x$ A
- $12 - x = 4$ A
- $12 = 4 \cdot x$ D

- $12 - 4 = x$ A
- $x = 12 - 4$ A
- $x + x + x + x = 12$ B

iM KH

## 1.3: Draw Diagrams for Equations

For each equation, draw a diagram and find the value of the unknown that makes the equation true.

1. $18 = 3 + x$

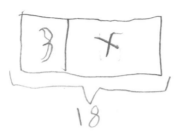

$x = 15$

2. $18 = 3 \cdot y$

$y = 6$

### Are you ready for more?

You are walking down a road, seeking treasure. The road branches off into three paths. A guard stands in each path. You know that only one of the guards is telling the truth, and the other two are lying. Here is what they say:

- Guard 1: The treasure lies down this path.
- Guard 2: No treasure lies down this path; seek elsewhere.
- Guard 3: The first guard is lying.

Which path leads to the treasure?

## Lesson 1 Summary

Tape diagrams can help us understand relationships between quantities and how operations describe those relationships.

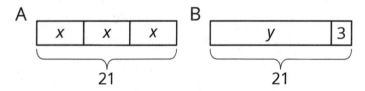

Diagram A has 3 parts that add to 21. Each part is labeled with the same letter, so we know the three parts are equal. Here are some equations that all represent diagram A:

$$x + x + x = 21$$

$$3 \cdot x = 21$$

$$x = 21 \div 3$$

$$x = \frac{1}{3} \cdot 21$$

Notice that the number 3 is not seen in the diagram; the 3 comes from counting 3 boxes representing 3 equal parts in 21.

We can use the diagram or any of the equations to reason that the value of $x$ is 7.

Diagram B has 2 parts that add to 21. Here are some equations that all represent diagram B:

$$y + 3 = 21$$

$$y = 21 - 3$$

$$3 = 21 - y$$

We can use the diagram or any of the equations to reason that the value of $y$ is 18.

iM KH

# Lesson 1 Practice Problems

1. Here is an equation: $x + 4 = 17$

   a. Draw a tape diagram to represent the equation.

   b. Which part of the diagram shows the quantity $x$? What about 4? What about 17?

   c. How does the diagram show that $x + 4$ has the same value as 17?

2. Diego is trying to find the value of $x$ in $5 \cdot x = 35$. He draws this diagram but is not certain how to proceed.

   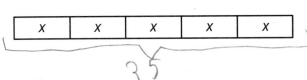

   a. Complete the tape diagram so it represents the equation $5 \cdot x = 35$.

   b. Find the value of $x$.

3. Match each equation to one of the two tape diagrams.

   a. $x + 3 = 9$

   b. $3 \cdot x = 9$

   c. $9 = 3 \cdot x$

   d. $3 + x = 9$

   e. $x = 9 - 3$

   f. $x = 9 \div 3$

   g. $x + x + x = 9$

   A
   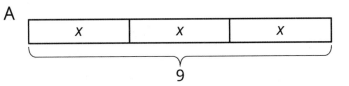

   B
   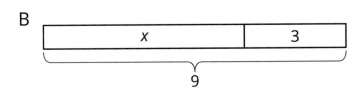

4. For each equation, draw a tape diagram and find the unknown value.

   a. $x + 9 = 16$

   b. $4 \cdot x = 28$

5. A shopper paid $2.52 for 4.5 pounds of potatoes, $7.75 for 2.5 pounds of broccoli, and $2.45 for 2.5 pounds of pears. What is the unit price of each item she bought? Show your reasoning.

(From Unit 5, Lesson 13.)

6. A sports drink bottle contains 16.9 fluid ounces. Andre drank 80% of the bottle. How many fluid ounces did Andre drink? Show your reasoning.

(From Unit 3, Lesson 14.)

7. The daily recommended allowance of calcium for a sixth grader is 1,200 mg. One cup of milk has 25% of the recommended daily allowance of calcium. How many milligrams of calcium are in a cup of milk? If you get stuck, consider using the double number line.

(From Unit 3, Lesson 11.)

iM KH

# Lesson 2: Truth and Equations

Let's use equations to represent stories and see what it means to solve equations.

## 2.1: Three Letters

1. The equation $a + b = c$ could be true or false.

    a. If $a$ is 3, $b$ is 4, and $c$ is 5, is the equation true or (false?)

    b. Find new values of $a$, $b$, and $c$ that make the equation true.

    $$1 + 4 = 5$$

    c. Find new values of $a$, $b$, and $c$ that make the equation false.

    $$3 + 7 = 5$$

2. The equation $x \cdot y = z$ could be true or false.

    a. If $x$ is 3, $y$ is 4, and $z$ is 12, is the equation (true) or false?

    b. Find new values of $x$, $y$, and $z$ that make the equation true.

    $$4 \times 3 = 12$$

    c. Find new values of $x$, $y$, and $z$ that make the equation false.

    $$784,860 \times 3 = 12$$

# 2.2: Storytime

Here are three situations and six equations. Which equation best represents each situation? If you get stuck, consider drawing a diagram.

$x + 5 = 20$          $x = 20 + 5$          $5x = 20$

$x + 20 = 5$          $5 \cdot 20 = x$          $20x = 5$

1. After Elena ran 5 miles on Friday, she had run a total of 20 miles for the week. She ran $x$ miles before Friday.

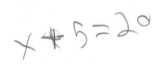

15

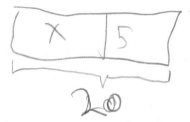

2. Andre's school has 20 clubs, which is five times as many as his cousin's school. His cousin's school has $x$ clubs.

4

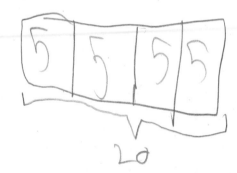

3. Jada volunteers at the animal shelter. She divided 5 cups of cat food equally to feed 20 cats. Each cat received $x$ cups of food.

$\frac{1}{4}$

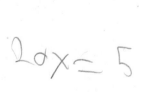

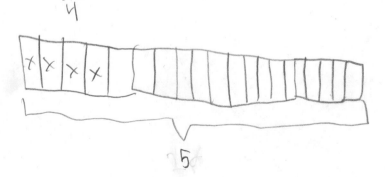

iM KH

## 2.3: Using Structure to Find Solutions

Here are some equations that contain a **variable** and a list of values. Think about what each equation means and find a **solution** in the list of values. If you get stuck, consider drawing a diagram. Be prepared to explain why your solution is correct.

1. $1000 - a = 400$   $\overset{600}{\phantom{x}}$  ~~600~~

2. $12.6 = b + 4.1$   $\overset{8.5}{\phantom{x}}$

3. $8c = 8$   $\overset{1}{\phantom{x}}$

4. $\frac{2}{3} \cdot d = \frac{10}{9}$   $\overset{5}{\underset{3}{\phantom{x}}}$

5. $10e = 1$

6. $10 = 0.5f$

7. $0.99 = 1 - g$

8. $h + \frac{3}{7} = 1$

List:   $\frac{1}{8}$   $\frac{3}{7}$   $\frac{4}{7}$   $\frac{3}{5}$   ~~$\frac{5}{3}$~~   $\frac{7}{3}$   0.01   0.1   0.5

      2      9.5   16.7   20   400   ~~600~~   1400

## Are you ready for more?

One solution to the equation $a + b + c = 10$ is $a = 2, b = 5, c = 3$.

How many different whole-number solutions are there to the equation $a + b + c = 10$? Explain or show your reasoning.

## Lesson 2 Summary

An equation can be true or false. An example of a true equation is $7 + 1 = 4 \cdot 2$. An example of a false equation is $7 + 1 = 9$.

An equation can have a letter in it, for example, $u + 1 = 8$. This equation is false if $u$ is 3, because $3 + 1$ does not equal 8. This equation is true if $u$ is 7, because $7 + 1 = 8$.

A letter in an equation is called a **variable**. In $u + 1 = 8$, the variable is $u$. A number that can be used in place of the variable that makes the equation true is called a **solution** to the equation. In $u + 1 = 8$, the solution is 7.

When a number is written next to a variable, the number and the variable are being multiplied. For example, $7x = 21$ means the same thing as $7 \cdot x = 21$. A number written next to a variable is called a **coefficient**. If no coefficient is written, the coefficient is 1. For example, in the equation $p + 3 = 5$, the coefficient of $p$ is 1.

## Glossary

- coefficient
- solution to an equation
- variable

# Lesson 2 Practice Problems

1. Select **all** the true equations.

    A. $5 + 0 = 0$

    B. $15 \cdot 0 = 0$

    C. $1.4 + 2.7 = 4.1$

    D. $\frac{2}{3} \cdot \frac{5}{9} = \frac{7}{12}$

    E. $4\frac{2}{3} = 5 - \frac{1}{3}$

2. Mai's water bottle had 24 ounces in it. After she drank $x$ ounces of water, there were 10 ounces left. Select **all** the equations that represent this situation.

    A. $24 \div 10 = x$

    B. $24 + 10 = x$

    C. $24 - 10 = x$

    D. $x + 10 = 24$

    E. $10x = 24$

3. Priya has 5 pencils, each $x$ inches in length. When she lines up the pencils end to end, they measure 34.5 inches. Select **all** the equations that represent this situation.

    A. $5 + x = 34.5$

    B. $5x = 34.5$

    C. $34.5 \div 5 = x$

    D. $34.5 - 5 = x$

    E. $x = (34.5) \cdot 5$

4. Match each equation with a solution from the list of values.

A. $2a = 4.6$

B. $b + 2 = 4.6$

C. $c \div 2 = 4.6$

D. $d - 2 = 4.6$

E. $e + \frac{3}{8} = 2$

F. $\frac{1}{8}f = 3$

G. $g \div \frac{8}{5} = 1$

1. $\frac{8}{5}$

2. $1\frac{5}{8}$

3. 2.3

4. 2.6

5. 6.6

6. 9.2

7. 24

5. The daily recommended allowance of vitamin C for a sixth grader is 45 mg. 1 orange has about 75% of the recommended daily allowance of vitamin C. How many milligrams are in 1 orange? If you get stuck, consider using the double number line.

vitamin C (mg)

(From Unit 3, Lesson 11.)

iM KH

6. There are 90 kids in the band. 20% of the kids own their own instruments, and the rest rent them.

   a. How many kids own their own instruments?

   b. How many kids rent instruments?

   c. What percentage of kids rent their instruments?

   (From Unit 3, Lesson 12.)

7. Find each product.

   a. $(0.25) \cdot (1.4)$

   b. $(0.061) \cdot (0.43)$

   c. $(1.017) \cdot (0.072)$

   d. $(5.226) \cdot (0.037)$

   (From Unit 5, Lesson 8.)

# Lesson 3: Staying in Balance

Let's use balanced hangers to help us solve equations.

## 3.1: Hanging Around

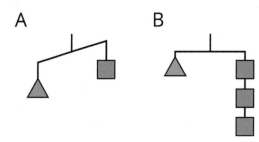

For diagram A, find:

1. One thing that *must* be true

   Triangle is heavery

2. One thing that *could* be true or false

   the hanger is streight

3. One thing that *cannot possibly* be true

   Spadre is equal to triangle.

For diagram B, find:

1. One thing that *must* be true

   The Same wight

2. One thing that *could* be true or false

   the triangle is 3pound and a square is 1pound

3. One thing that *cannot possibly* be true

   thier not equal

iM KH

# 3.2: Match Equations and Hangers

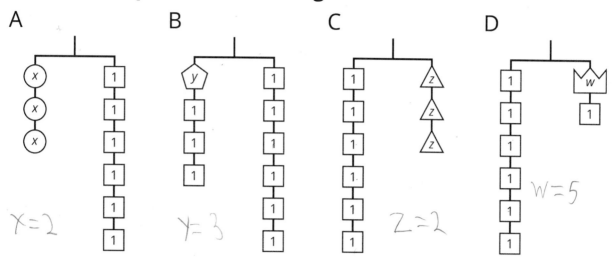

A   B   C   D

X=2   Y=3   Z=2   W=5

1. Match each hanger to an equation. Complete the equation by writing $x$, $y$, $z$, or $w$ in the empty box.

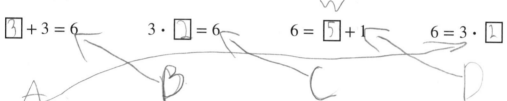

$$\boxed{x} + 3 = 6 \qquad 3 \cdot \boxed{y} = 6 \qquad 6 = \boxed{w} + 1 \qquad 6 = 3 \cdot \boxed{z}$$

A   B   C   D

2. Find a solution to each equation. Use the hangers to explain what each solution means.

# 3.3: Connecting Diagrams to Equations and Solutions

Here are some balanced hangers. Each piece is labeled with its weight.

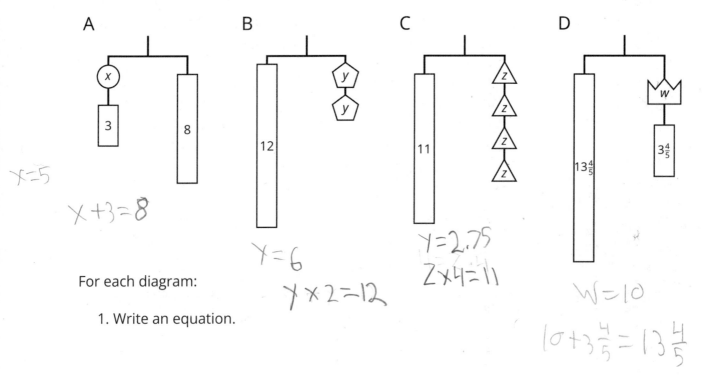

$x=5$

$x+3=8$

$y=6$

$y \times 2 = 12$

$y=2.75$

$z \times 4 = 11$

$w=10$

$10+3\frac{4}{5}=13\frac{4}{5}$

For each diagram:

1. Write an equation.

2. Explain how to reason with the *diagram* to find the weight of a piece with a letter.

3. Explain how to reason with the *equation* to find the weight of a piece with a letter.

## Are you ready for more?

When you have the time, visit the site https://solveme.edc.org/Mobiles.html to solve some trickier puzzles that use hanger diagrams like the ones in this lesson. You can even build new ones. (If you want to do this during class, check with your teacher first!)

iM KH

## Lesson 3 Summary

A hanger stays balanced when the weights on both sides are equal. We can change the weights and the hanger will stay balanced as long as both sides are changed in the same way. For example, adding 2 pounds to each side of a balanced hanger will keep it balanced. Removing half of the weight from each side will also keep it balanced.

An equation can be compared to a balanced hanger. We can change the equation, but for a true equation to remain true, the same thing must be done to both sides of the equal sign. If we add or subtract the same number on each side, or multiply or divide each side by the same number, the new equation will still be true.

This way of thinking can help us find solutions to equations. Instead of checking different values, we can think about subtracting the same amount from each side or dividing each side by the same number.

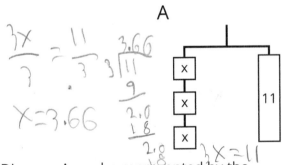

A

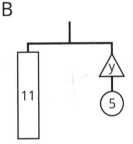

B

Diagram A can be represented by the equation $3x = 11$.

Diagram B can be represented with the equation $11 = y + 5$.

If we break the 11 into 3 equal parts, each part will have the same weight as a block with an $x$.

If we remove a weight of 5 from each side of the hanger, it will stay in balance.

Splitting each side of the hanger into 3 equal parts is the same as dividing each side of the equation by 3.

Removing 5 from each side of the hanger is the same as subtracting 5 from each side of the equation.

- $3x$ divided by 3 is $x$.

- 11 divided by 3 is $\frac{11}{3}$.

- If $3x = 11$ is true, then $x = \frac{11}{3}$ is true.

- The solution to $3x = 11$ is $\frac{11}{3}$.

- $11 - 5$ is 6.

- $y + 5 - 5$ is $y$.

- If $11 = y + 5$ is true, then $6 = y$ is true.

- The solution to $11 = y + 5$ is 6.

# Lesson 3 Practice Problems

1. Select **all** the equations that represent the hanger.

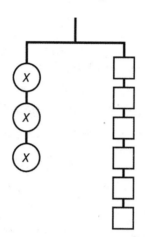

A. $x + x + x = 1 + 1 + 1 + 1 + 1 + 1$

B. $x \cdot x \cdot x = 6$

C. $3x = 6$

D. $x + 3 = 6$

E. $x \cdot x \cdot x = 1 \cdot 1 \cdot 1 \cdot 1 \cdot 1 \cdot 1$

2. Write an equation to represent each hanger.

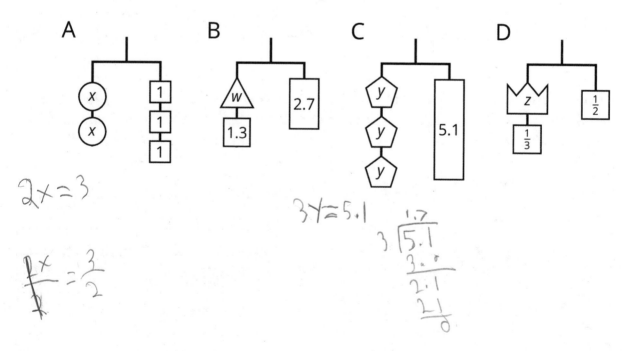

$2x = 3$

$\frac{2x}{2} = \frac{3}{2}$

$3y = 5.1$

$\begin{array}{r} 1.7 \\ 3\overline{)5.1} \\ 3.0 \\ \hline 2.1 \\ 2.1 \\ \hline 0 \end{array}$

iM KH

3.  a. Write an equation to represent the hanger.

    b. Explain how to reason with the hanger to find the value of $x$.

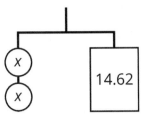

    c. Explain how to reason with the equation to find the value of $x$.

4. Andre says that $x$ is 7 because he can move the two 1s with the $x$ to the other side.

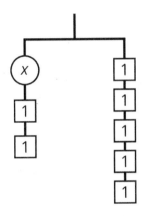

Do you agree with Andre? Explain your reasoning.

5. Match each equation to one of the diagrams.

    a. $12 - m = 4$

    b. $12 = 4 \cdot m$

    c. $m - 4 = 12$

    d. $\frac{m}{4} = 12$

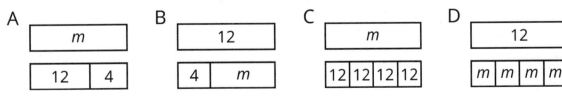

(From Unit 6, Lesson 1.)

6. The area of a rectangle is 14 square units. It has side lengths $x$ and $y$. Given each value for $x$, find $y$.

   a. $x = 2\frac{1}{3}$

   b. $x = 4\frac{1}{5}$

   c. $x = \frac{7}{6}$

   (From Unit 4, Lesson 13.)

7. Lin needs to save up $20 for a new game. How much money does she have if she has saved each percentage of her goal. Explain your reasoning.

   a. 25%

   b. 75%

   c. 125%

   (From Unit 3, Lesson 11.)

iM KH

# Lesson 4: Practice Solving Equations and Representing Situations with Equations

Let's solve equations by doing the same to each side.

## 4.1: Number Talk: Subtracting From Five

Find the value of each expression mentally.

$5 - 2$   3

$5 - 2.1$   2.9

$5 - 2.17$   1.93

$5 - 2\frac{7}{8}$   $2\frac{1}{8}$

# 4.2: Row Game: Solving Equations Practice

Solve the equations in one column. Your partner will work on the other column.

Check in with your partner after you finish each row. Your answers in each row should be the same. If your answers aren't the same, work together to find the error and correct it.

| column A | column B |
|---|---|
| $18 = 2x$   9 | $36 = 4x$   9 |
| $17 = x + 9$   8 | $13 = x + 5$   8 |
| $8x = 56$   7 | $3x = 21$   7 |
| $21 = \frac{1}{4}x$   84 | $28 = \frac{1}{3}x$   84 |
| $6x = 45$   7.5 | $8x = 60$   7.5 |
| $x + 4\frac{5}{6} = 9$   $4\frac{1}{6}$ | $x + 3\frac{5}{6} = 8$   $4\frac{1}{6}$ |
| $\frac{5}{7}x = 55$   77 | 77   $\frac{3}{7}x = 33$ |
| $\frac{1}{5} = 6x$   $\frac{1}{30}$ | $\frac{1}{3} = 10x$   $\frac{1}{30}$ |
| $2.17 + x = 5$   2.83 | $6.17 + x = 9$   2.83 |
| $\frac{20}{3} = \frac{10}{9}x$   6 | $\frac{14}{5} = \frac{7}{15}x$   6 |
| $14.88 + x = 17.05$   2.17 | $3.91 + x = 6.08$   2.17 |
| $3\frac{3}{4}x = 1\frac{1}{4}$   $\frac{1}{3}$ | $\frac{7}{5}x = \frac{7}{15}$   $\frac{1}{3}$ |

# 4.3: Choosing Equations to Match Situations

Circle **all** of the equations that describe each situation. If you get stuck, consider drawing a diagram. Then find the solution for each situation.

1. Clare has 8 fewer books than Mai. If Mai has 26 books, how many books does Clare have?

   - ○ $26 - x = 8$
   - ○ $x = 26 + 8$
   - ○ $x + 8 = 26$
   - ○ $26 - 8 = x$

   $x = \underline{18}$

2. A coach formed teams of 8 from all the players in a soccer league. There are 14 teams. How many players are in the league?

   - ○ $y = 14 \div 8$
   - ○ $\frac{y}{8} = 14$
   - ○ $\frac{1}{8}y = 14$
   - ○ $y = 14 \cdot 8$

   $y = \underline{112}$

3. Kiran scored 223 more points in a computer game than Tyler. If Kiran scored 409 points, how many points did Tyler score?

   - ○ $223 = 409 - z$
   - ○ $409 - 223 = z$
   - ○ $409 + 223 = z$
   - ○ $409 = 223 + z$

   $z = \underline{186}$

4. Mai ran 27 miles last week, which was three times as far as Jada ran. How far did Jada run?

   - ○ $3w = 27$
   - ○ $w = \frac{1}{3} \cdot 27$
   - ○ $w = 27 \div 3$
   - ○ $w = 3 \cdot 27$

   $w = \underline{9}$

**Are you ready for more?**

Mai's mother was 28 when Mai was born. Mai is now 12 years old. In how many years will Mai's mother be twice Mai's age? How old will they be then?

**Lesson 4 Summary**

Writing and solving equations can help us answer questions about situations.

Suppose a scientist has 13.68 liters of acid and needs 16.05 liters for an experiment. How many more liters of acid does she need for the experiment?

- We can represent this situation with the equation: $13.68 + x = 16.05$

- When working with hangers, we saw that the solution can be found by subtracting 13.68 from each side. This gives us some new equations that also represent the situation:

$$x = 16.05 - 13.68$$
$$x = 2.37$$

- Finding a solution in this way leads to a variable on one side of the equal sign and a number on the other. We can easily read the solution—in this case, 2.37—from an equation with a letter on one side and a number on the other. We often write solutions in this way.

Let's say a food pantry takes a 54-pound bag of rice and splits it into portions that each weigh $\frac{3}{4}$ of a pound. How many portions can they make from this bag?

- We can represent this situation with the equation:

$$\frac{3}{4}x = 54$$

- We can find the value of $x$ by dividing each side by $\frac{3}{4}$. This gives us some new equations that represent the same situation:

$$x = 54 \div \frac{3}{4}$$
$$x = 72$$

- The solution is 72 portions.

iM KH

# Lesson 5: A New Way to Interpret $a$ over $b$

Let's investigate what a fraction means when the numerator and denominator are not whole numbers.

## 5.1: Recalling Ways of Solving

Solve each equation. Be prepared to explain your reasoning.

$0.07 = 10m$ $\qquad\qquad\qquad\qquad 10.1 = t + 7.2$

## 5.2: Interpreting $\frac{a}{b}$

Solve each equation.

1. $35 = 7x$

2. $35 = 11x$

3. $7x = 7.7$

4. $0.3x = 2.1$

5. $\frac{2}{5} = \frac{1}{2}x$

**Are you ready for more?**

Solve the equation. Try to find some shortcuts.

$$\frac{1}{6} \cdot \frac{3}{20} \cdot \frac{5}{42} \cdot \frac{7}{72} \cdot x = \frac{1}{384}$$

## 5.3: Storytime Again

Take turns with your partner telling a story that might be represented by each equation. Then, for each equation, choose one story, state what quantity $x$ describes, and solve the equation. If you get stuck, consider drawing a diagram.

$$0.7 + x = 12 \qquad\qquad\qquad \frac{1}{4}x = \frac{3}{2}$$

## Lesson 5 Summary

In the past, you learned that a fraction such as $\frac{4}{5}$ can be thought of in a few ways.

- $\frac{4}{5}$ is a number you can locate on the number line by dividing the section between 0 and 1 into 5 equal parts and then counting 4 of those parts to the right of 0.

- $\frac{4}{5}$ is the share that each person would have if 4 wholes were shared equally among 5 people. This means that $\frac{4}{5}$ is the result of *dividing* 4 by 5.

We can extend this meaning of *a fraction as a quotient* to fractions whose numerators and denominators are not whole numbers. For example, we can represent 4.5 pounds of rice divided into portions that each weigh 1.5 pounds as: $\frac{4.5}{1.5} = 4.5 \div 1.5 = 3$. In other words, $\frac{4.5}{1.5} = 3$ because the quotient of 4.5 and 1.5 is 3.

Fractions that involve non-whole numbers can also be used when we solve equations.

Suppose a road under construction is $\frac{3}{8}$ finished and the length of the completed part is $\frac{4}{3}$ miles. How long will the road be when completed?

We can write the equation $\frac{3}{8}x = \frac{4}{3}$ to represent the situation and solve the equation.

The completed road will be $3\frac{5}{9}$ or about 3.6 miles long.

$$\frac{3}{8}x = \frac{4}{3}$$

$$x = \frac{\frac{4}{3}}{\frac{3}{8}}$$

$$x = \frac{4}{3} \cdot \frac{8}{3}$$

$$x = \frac{32}{9} = 3\frac{5}{9}$$

# Lesson 5 Practice Problems

1. Select **all** the expressions that equal $\frac{3.15}{0.45}$.

    A. $(3.15) \cdot (0.45)$

    B. $(3.15) \div (0.45)$

    C. $(3.15) \cdot \frac{1}{0.45}$

    D. $(3.15) \div \frac{45}{100}$

    E. $(3.15) \cdot \frac{100}{45}$

    F. $\frac{0.45}{3.15}$

2. Which expressions are solutions to the equation $\frac{3}{4}x = 15$? Select **all** that apply.

    A. $\frac{15}{\frac{3}{4}}$

    B. $\frac{15}{\frac{4}{3}}$

    C. $\frac{4}{3} \cdot 15$

    D. $\frac{3}{4} \cdot 15$

    E. $15 \div \frac{3}{4}$

3. Solve each equation.

    $4a = 32$          $4 = 32b$          $10c = 26$          $26 = 100d$

iM KH

4. For each equation, write a story problem represented by the equation. For each equation, state what quantity $x$ represents. If you get stuck, consider drawing a diagram.

a. $\frac{3}{4} + x = 2$

b. $1.5x = 6$

5. Write as many mathematical expressions or equations as you can about the image. Include a fraction, a decimal number, or a percentage in each.

(From Unit 3, Lesson 13.)

6. In a lilac paint mixture, 40% of the mixture is white paint, 20% is blue, and the rest is red. There are 4 cups of blue paint used in a batch of lilac paint.

    a. How many cups of white paint are used?

    b. How many cups of red paint are used?

    c. How many cups of lilac paint will this batch yield?

If you get stuck, consider using a tape diagram.

(From Unit 3, Lesson 12.)

7. Triangle P has a base of 12 inches and a corresponding height of 8 inches. Triangle Q has a base of 15 inches and a corresponding height of 6.5 inches. Which triangle has a greater area? Show your reasoning.

(From Unit 1, Lesson 9.)

iM KH

# Lesson 6: Write Expressions Where Letters Stand for Numbers

Let's use expressions with variables to describe situations.

## 6.1: Algebra Talk: When $x$ is 6

If $x$ is 6, what is:

$x + 4$   10

$7 - x$   1

$x^2$   36

$\frac{1}{3}x$   2

## 6.2: Lemonade Sales and Heights

1. Lin set up a lemonade stand. She sells the lemonade for $0.50 per cup.

   a. Complete the table to show how much money she would collect if she sold each number of cups.

   | lemonade sold (number of cups) | 12 | 183 | $c$ | 255 |
   |---|---|---|---|---|
   | money collected (dollars) | 6 | 91.5 | .5c | 127.50 |

   b. How many cups did she sell if she collected $127.50? Be prepared to explain your reasoning.

2. Elena is 59 inches tall. Some other people are taller than Elena.

a. Complete the table to show the height of each person.

| person | Andre | Lin | Noah |
|---|---|---|---|
| how much taller than Elena (inches) | 4 | $6\frac{1}{2}$ | $d$ |
| person's height (inches) | 63 | $65\frac{1}{2}$ | $59+d$ |

b. If Noah is $64\frac{3}{4}$ inches tall, how much taller is he than Elena?

$5\frac{3}{4}$

# 6.3: Building Expressions

1. Clare is 5 years older than her cousin.

a. How old would Clare be if her cousin is:

10 years old?    15

2 years old?    7

$x$ years old?    $5+x$

b. Clare is 12 years old. How old is Clare's cousin?

iM KH

2. Diego has 3 times as many comic books as Han.

 a. How many comic books does Diego have if Han has:

 6 comic books? 18

 *n* books? 3n

 b. Diego has 27 comic books. How many comic books does Han have?
 9

3. Two fifths of the vegetables in Priya's garden are tomatoes.

 a. How many tomatoes are there if Priya's garden has:

 20 vegetables? 8

 *x* vegetables? $\frac{3}{5}$ ✓

 b. Priya's garden has 6 tomatoes. How many total vegetables are there? 20

 15

 $3 \times \frac{5}{1} = 15$

4. A school paid $31.25 for each calculator.

 a. If the school bought *x* calculators, how much did they pay?

 b. The school spent $500 on calculators. How many did the school buy?

## Are you ready for more?

Kiran, Mai, Jada, and Tyler went to their school carnival. They all won chips that they could exchange for prizes. Kiran won $\frac{2}{3}$ as many chips as Jada. Mai won 4 times as many chips as Kiran. Tyler won half as many chips as Mai.

1. Write an expression for the number of chips Tyler won. You should only use one variable: $J$, which stands for the number of chips Jada won.

2. If Jada won 42 chips, how many chips did Tyler, Kiran, and Mai each win?

## Lesson 6 Summary

Suppose you share a birthday with a neighbor, but she is 3 years older than you. When you were 1, she was 4. When you were 9, she was 12. When you are 42, she will be 45.

If we let $a$ represent your age at any time, your neighbor's age can be expressed $a + 3$.

| your age | 1 | 9 | 42 | $a$ |
|---|---|---|---|---|
| neighbor's age | 4 | 12 | 45 | $a + 3$ |

We often use a letter such as $x$ or $a$ as a placeholder for a number in expressions. These are called *variables* (just like the letters we used in equations, previously). Variables make it possible to write expressions that represent a calculation even when we don't know all the numbers in the calculation.

How old will you be when your neighbor is 32? Since your neighbor's age is calculated with the expression $a + 3$, we can write the equation $a + 3 = 32$. When your neighbor is 32 you will be 29, because $a + 3 = 32$ is true when $a$ is 29.

iM KH

# Lesson 6 Practice Problems

1. Instructions for a craft project say that the length of a piece of red ribbon should be 7 inches less than the length of a piece of blue ribbon.

    a. How long is the red ribbon if the length of the blue ribbon is:

    10 inches?                27 inches?                $x$ inches?

    b. How long is the blue ribbon if the red ribbon is 12 inches?

2. Tyler has 3 times as many books as Mai.

    a. How many books does Mai have if Tyler has:

    15 books?                21 books?                $x$ books?

    b. Tyler has 18 books. How many books does Mai have?

3. A bottle holds 24 ounces of water. It has $x$ ounces of water in it.

    a. What does $24 - x$ represent in this situation?

    b. Write a question about this situation that has $24 - x$ for the answer.

4. Write an equation represented by this tape diagram using each of these operations.

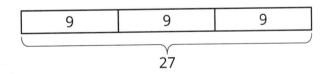

    a. addition

    b. subtraction

    c. multiplication

    d. division

(From Unit 6, Lesson 1.)

5. Select **all** the equations that describe each situation and then find the solution.

    a. Han's house is 450 meters from school. Lin's house is 135 meters closer to school. How far is Lin's house from school?

        ■ $z = 450 + 135$

        ■ $z = 450 - 135$

        ■ $z - 135 = 450$

        ■ $z + 135 = 450$

    b. Tyler's playlist has 36 songs. Noah's playlist has one quarter as many songs as Tyler's playlist. How many songs are on Noah's playlist?

        ■ $w = 4 \cdot 36$

        ■ $w = 36 \div 4$

        ■ $4w = 36$

        ■ $\frac{w}{4} = 36$

(From Unit 6, Lesson 4.)

6. You had $50. You spent 10% of the money on clothes, 20% on games, and the rest on books. How much money was spent on books?

(From Unit 3, Lesson 12.)

7. A trash bin has a capacity of 50 gallons. What percentage of its capacity is each amount? Show your reasoning.

    a. 5 gallons

    b. 30 gallons

    c. 45 gallons

    d. 100 gallons

(From Unit 3, Lesson 14.)

iM KH

# Lesson 7: Revisit Percentages

Let's use equations to find percentages.

## 7.1: Number Talk: Percentages

Solve each problem mentally.

1. Bottle A contains 4 ounces of water, which is 25% of the amount of water in Bottle B. How much water is there in Bottle B?

2. Bottle C contains 150% of the water in Bottle B. How much water is there in Bottle C?

3. Bottle D contains 12 ounces of water. What percentage of the amount of water in Bottle B is this?

## 7.2: Representing a Percentage Problem with an Equation

1. Answer each question and show your reasoning.

   a. Is 60% of 400 equal to 87?

   b. Is 60% of 200 equal to 87?

   c. Is 60% of 120 equal to 87?

2. 60% of $x$ is equal to 87. Write an equation that expresses the relationship between 60%, $x$, and 87. Solve your equation.

3. Write an equation to help you find the value of each variable. Solve the equation.

60% of $c$ is 43.2.                                    38% of $e$ is 190.

# 7.3: Puppies Grow Up, Revisited

1. Puppy A weighs 8 pounds, which is about 25% of its adult weight. What will be the adult weight of Puppy A?

2. Puppy B weighs 8 pounds, which is about 75% of its adult weight. What will be the adult weight of Puppy B?

3. If you haven't already, write an equation for each situation. Then, show how you could find the adult weight of each puppy by solving the equation.

iM KH

## Are you ready for more?

Diego wants to paint his room purple. He bought one gallon of purple paint that is 30% red paint and 70% blue paint. Diego wants to add more blue to the mix so that the paint mixture is 20% red, 80% blue.

1. How much blue paint should Diego add? Test the following possibilities: 0.2 gallons, 0.3 gallons, 0.4 gallons, 0.5 gallons.

2. Write an equation in which $x$ represents the amount of paint Diego should add.

3. Check that the amount of paint Diego should add is a solution to your equation.

## Lesson 7 Summary

If we know that 455 students are in school today and that number represents 70% attendance, we can write an equation to figure out how many students go to the school.

The number of students in school today is known in two different ways: as 70% of the students in the school, and also as 455. If $s$ represents the total number of students who go to the school, then 70% of $s$, or $\frac{70}{100}s$, represents the number of students that are in school today, which is 455.

We can write and solve the equation:

$$\frac{70}{100}s = 455$$
$$s = 455 \div \frac{70}{100}$$
$$s = 455 \cdot \frac{100}{70}$$
$$s = 650$$

There are 650 students in the school.

In general, equations can help us solve problems in which one amount is a percentage of another amount.

# Lesson 7 Practice Problems

1. A crew has paved $\frac{3}{4}$ of a mile of road. If they have completed 50% of the work, how long is the road they are paving?

2. 40% of $x$ is 35.

   a. Write an equation that shows the relationship of 40%, $x$, and 35.

   b. Use your equation to find $x$. Show your reasoning.

3. Priya has completed 9 exam questions. This is 60% of the questions on the exam.

   a. Write an equation representing this situation. Explain the meaning of any variables you use.

   b. How many questions are on the exam? Show your reasoning.

4. Answer each question. Show your reasoning.

   20% of $a$ is 11. What is $a$?                    75% of $b$ is 12. What is $b$?

   80% of $c$ is 20. What is $c$?                    200% of $d$ is 18. What is $d$?

iM KH

5. For the equation $2n - 3 = 7$

    a. What is the variable?

    b. What is the coefficient of the variable?

    c. Which of these is the solution to the equation? 2, 3, 5, 7, $n$

(From Unit 6, Lesson 2.)

6. Which of these is a solution to the equation $\frac{1}{8} = \frac{2}{5} \cdot x$?

    A. $\frac{2}{40}$

    B. $\frac{5}{16}$

    C. $\frac{11}{40}$

    D. $\frac{17}{40}$

(From Unit 6, Lesson 2.)

7. Find the quotients.

    a. $0.009 \div 0.001$

    b. $0.009 \div 0.002$

    c. $0.0045 \div 0.001$

    d. $0.0045 \div 0.002$

(From Unit 5, Lesson 13.)

# Lesson 8: Equal and Equivalent

Let's use diagrams to figure out which expressions are equivalent and which are just sometimes equal.

## 8.1: Algebra Talk: Solving Equations by Seeing Structure

Find a solution to each equation mentally.

$3 + x = 8$  5

$10 = 12 - x$  2

$x^2 = 49$  7²

$\frac{1}{3}x = 6$  18

## 8.2: Using Diagrams to Show That Expressions are Equivalent

Here is a diagram of $x + 2$ and $3x$ when $x$ is 4. Notice that the two diagrams are lined up on their left sides.

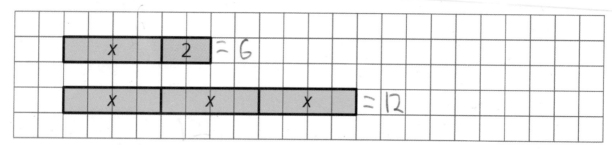

In each of your drawings below, line up the diagrams on one side.

1. Draw a diagram of $x + 2$, and a separate diagram of $3x$, when $x$ is 3.  ✗

iM KH

2. Draw a diagram of $x + 2$, and a separate diagram of $3x$, when $x$ is 2. ✗

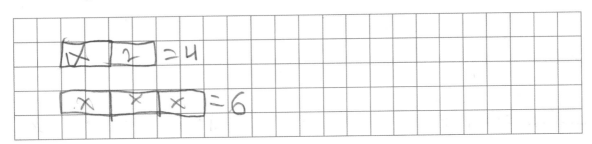

3. Draw a diagram of $x + 2$, and a separate diagram of $3x$, when $x$ is 1. ✓

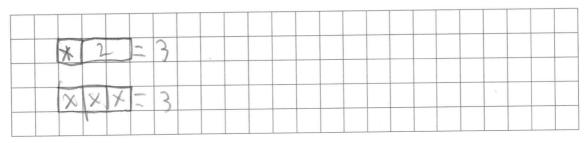

4. Draw a diagram of $x + 2$, and a separate diagram of $3x$, when $x$ is 0. ✗

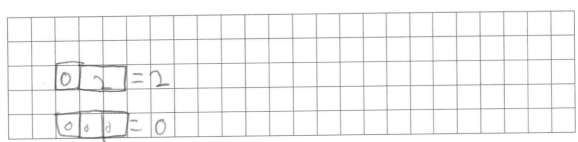

5. When are $x + 2$ and $3x$ equal? When are they not equal? Use your diagrams to explain.

x=1 is equal        not equal x=5

6. Draw a diagram of $x + 3$, and a separate diagram of $3 + x$.

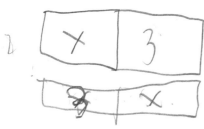

7. When are $x + 3$ and $3 + x$ equal? When are they not equal? Use your diagrams to explain. They are equal when x = any number

when the 2 numbers are not equal

## 8.3: Identifying Equivalent Expressions

Here is a list of expressions. Find any pairs of expressions that are equivalent. If you get stuck, try reasoning with diagrams.

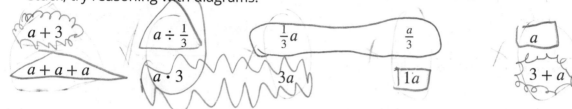

$a + 3$

$a + a + a$

$a \div \frac{1}{3}$

$a \cdot 3$

$\frac{1}{3}a$

$3a$

$\frac{a}{3}$

$1a$

$a$

$3 + a$

**Are you ready for more?**

Below are four questions about equivalent expressions. For each one:

- Decide whether you think the expressions are equivalent.
- Test your guess by choosing numbers for $x$ (and $y$, if needed).

1. Are $\dfrac{x \cdot x \cdot x \cdot x}{x}$ and $x \cdot x \cdot x$ equivalent expressions?

2. Are $\dfrac{x + x + x + x}{x}$ and $x + x + x$ equivalent expressions?

3. Are $2(x + y)$ and $2x + 2y$ equivalent expressions?

4. Are $2xy$ and $2x \cdot 2y$ equivalent expressions?

iM KH

## Lesson 8 Summary

We can use diagrams showing lengths of rectangles to see when expressions are equal. For example, the expressions $x + 9$ and $4x$ are equal when $x$ is 3, but are not equal for other values of $x$.

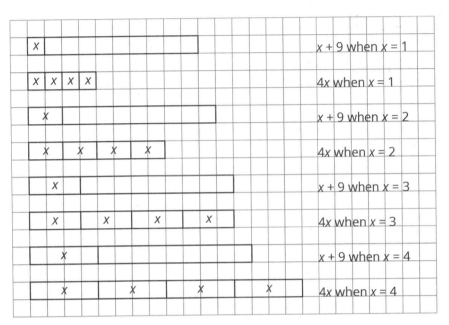

Sometimes two expressions are equal for only one particular value of their variable. Other times, they seem to be equal no matter what the value of the variable.

Expressions that are always equal for the same value of their variable are called **equivalent expressions**. However, it would be impossible to test every possible value of the variable. How can we know for sure that expressions are equivalent? We use the meaning of operations and properties of operations to know that expressions are equivalent. Here are some examples:

- $x + 3$ is equivalent to $3 + x$ because of the commutative property of addition.
- $4 \cdot y$ is equivalent to $y \cdot 4$ because of the commutative property of multiplication.
- $a + a + a + a + a$ is equivalent to $5 \cdot a$ because adding 5 copies of something is the same as multiplying it by 5.
- $b \div 3$ is equivalent to $b \cdot \frac{1}{3}$ because dividing by a number is the same as multiplying by its reciprocal.

In the coming lessons, we will see how another property, the distributive property, can show that expressions are equivalent.

### Glossary

- equivalent expressions

# Lesson 8 Practice Problems

1. a. Draw a diagram of $x + 3$ and a diagram of $2x$ when $x$ is 1.

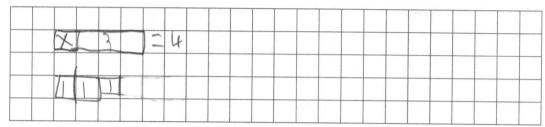

   b. Draw a diagram of $x + 3$ and of $2x$ when $x$ is 2.

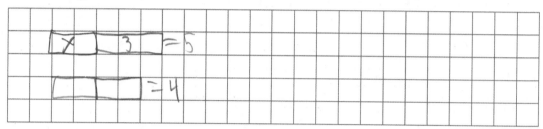

   c. Draw a diagram of $x + 3$ and of $2x$ when $x$ is 3.

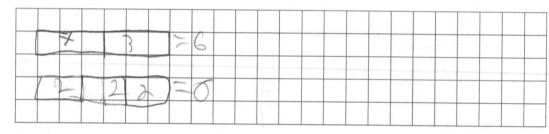

   d. Draw a diagram of $x + 3$ and of $2x$ when $x$ is 4.

   e. When are $x + 3$ and $2x$ equal? When are they not equal? Use your diagrams to explain.

iM KH

2.   a. Do $4x$ and $15 + x$ have the same value when $x$ is 5?

yes

b. Are $4x$ and $15 + x$ equivalent expressions? Explain your reasoning.

No b/c $\frac{4x}{2} = 8$   $\frac{15 + x}{2} = 17$

3.   a. Check that $2b + b$ and $3b$ have the same value when $b$ is 1, 2, and 3.

b. Do $2b + b$ and $3b$ have the same value for all values of $b$? Explain your reasoning.

c. Are $2b + b$ and $3b$ equivalent expressions?

4. 80% of $x$ is equal to 100.

a. Write an equation that shows the relationship of 80%, $x$, and 100.

b. Use your equation to find $x$.

(From Unit 6, Lesson 7.)

5. For each story problem, write an equation to represent the problem and then solve the equation. Be sure to explain the meaning of any variables you use.

 a. Jada's dog was $5\frac{1}{2}$ inches tall when it was a puppy. Now her dog is $14\frac{1}{2}$ inches taller than that. How tall is Jada's dog now?

 b. Lin picked $9\frac{3}{4}$ pounds of apples, which was 3 times the weight of the apples Andre picked. How many pounds of apples did Andre pick?

(From Unit 6, Lesson 5.)

6. Find these products.

 a. $(2.3) \cdot (1.4)$

 b. $(1.72) \cdot (2.6)$

 c. $(18.2) \cdot (0.2)$

 d. $15 \cdot (1.2)$

(From Unit 5, Lesson 8.)

7. Calculate $141.75 \div 2.5$ using a method of your choice. Show or explain your reasoning.

(From Unit 5, Lesson 13.)

iM KH

# Lesson 9: The Distributive Property, Part 1

Let's use the distributive property to make calculating easier.

## 9.1: Number Talk: Ways to Multiply

Find each product mentally.

$5 \cdot 102$

$5 \cdot 98$

$5 \cdot 999$

## 9.2: Ways to Represent Area of a Rectangle

1. Select **all** the expressions that represent the area of the large, outer rectangle in figure A. Explain your reasoning.

    A

    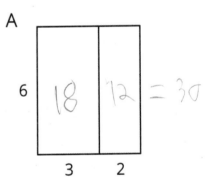

   - ~~6 + 3 + 2~~
   - ⬤ $6 \cdot 3 + 6 \cdot 2$
   - ○ $6 \cdot 3 + 2$
   - ⬤ $6 \cdot 5$
   - ⬤ $6(3 + 2)$
   - ○ $6 \cdot 3 \cdot 2$

2. Select **all** the expressions that represent the area of the shaded rectangle on the left side of figure B. Explain your reasoning.

    B

    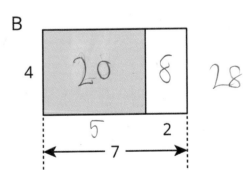

   - ~~4 · 7 + 4 · 2~~
   - ~~4 · 7 · 2~~
   - ⬤ $4 \cdot 5$
   - ⬤ $4 \cdot 7 - 4 \cdot 2$
   - ⬤ $4(7 - 2)$
   - ~~4(7 + 2)~~
   - ~~4 · 2 - 4 · 7~~

## 9.3: Distributive Practice

Complete the table. If you get stuck, skip an entry and come back to it, or consider drawing a diagram of two rectangles that share a side.

| column 1 | column 2 | column 3 | column 4 | value |
|---|---|---|---|---|
| $5 \cdot 98$ | $5(100 - 2)$ | $5 \cdot 100 - 5 \cdot 2$ | $500 - 10$ | 490 |
| $33 \cdot 12$ | $33(10 + 2)$ | | | |
| | | $3 \cdot 10 - 3 \cdot 4$ | $30 - 12$ | |
| | $100(0.04 + 0.06)$ | | | |
| | | $8 \cdot \frac{1}{2} + 8 \cdot \frac{1}{4}$ | | |
| | | | $9 + 12$ | |
| | | | $24 - 16$ | |

iM KH

## Are you ready for more?

1. Use the distributive property to write two expressions that equal 360. (There are many correct ways to do this.)

2. Is it possible to write an expression like $a(b + c)$ that equals 360 where $a$ is a fraction? Either write such an expression, or explain why it is impossible.

3. Is it possible to write an expression like $a(b - c)$ that equals 360? Either write such an expression, or explain why it is impossible.

4. How many ways do you think there are to make 360 using the distributive property?

## Lesson 9 Summary

A **term** is a single number or variable, or variables and numbers multiplied together. Some examples of terms are 10, $8x$, $ab$, and $7yz$.

When we need to do mental calculations, we often come up with ways to make the calculation easier to do mentally.

Suppose we are grocery shopping and need to know how much it will cost to buy 5 cans of beans at 79 cents a can. We may calculate mentally in this way:

$$5 \cdot 79$$
$$5 \cdot 70 + 5 \cdot 9$$
$$350 + 45$$
$$395$$

In general, when we multiply two terms (or factors), we can break up one of the factors into parts, multiply each part by the other factor, and then add the products. The result will be the same as the product of the two original factors. When we break up one of the factors and multiply the parts we are using the distributive property.

The distributive property also works with subtraction. Here is another way to find $5 \cdot 79$:

$$5 \cdot 79$$
$$5 \cdot (80 - 1)$$
$$400 - 5$$
$$395$$

## Glossary

- term

## Lesson 9 Practice Problems

1. Select **all** the expressions that represent the area of the large, outer rectangle.

   A. $5(2 + 4)$

   B. $5 \cdot 2 + 4$

   C. $5 \cdot 2 + 5 \cdot 4$

   D. $5 \cdot 2 \cdot 4$

   E. $5 + 2 + 4$

   F. $5 \cdot 6$

2. Draw and label diagrams that show these two methods for calculating $19 \cdot 50$.

   ○ First find $10 \cdot 50$ and then add $9 \cdot 50$.

   ○ First find $20 \cdot 50$ and then take away 50.

3. Complete each calculation using the distributive property.

   $98 \cdot 24$
   $(100 - 2) \cdot 24$
   $\ldots$

   $21 \cdot 15$
   $(20 + 1) \cdot 15$
   $\ldots$

   $0.51 \cdot 40$
   $(0.5 + 0.01) \cdot 40$
   $\ldots$

4. A group of 8 friends go to the movies. A bag of popcorn costs $2.99. How much will it cost to get one bag of popcorn for each friend? Explain how you can calculate this amount mentally.

iM KH

5.  a. On graph paper, draw diagrams of $a + a + a + a$ and $4a$ when $a$ is 1, 2, and 3. What do you notice?

    b. Do $a + a + a + a$ and $4a$ have the same value for any value of $a$? Explain how you know.

(From Unit 6, Lesson 8.)

6. 120% of $x$ is equal to 78.

    a. Write an equation that shows the relationship of 120%, $x$, and 78.

    b. Use your equation to find $x$. Show your reasoning.

(From Unit 6, Lesson 7.)

7. Kiran's aunt is 17 years older than Kiran.

    a. How old will Kiran's aunt be when Kiran is:

    15 years old?          30 years old?          $x$ years old?

    b. How old will Kiran be when his aunt is 60 years old?

(From Unit 6, Lesson 6.)

# Lesson 10: The Distributive Property, Part 2

Let's use rectangles to understand the distributive property with variables.

## 10.1: Possible Areas

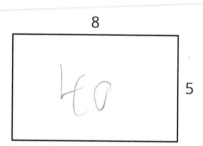

1. A rectangle has a width of 4 units and a length of $m$ units. Write an expression for the area of this rectangle.

   $4m$

2. What is the area of the rectangle if $m$ is:

   3 units?           2.2 units?           $\frac{1}{5}$ unit?

   $12$                $8.8$                $\frac{4}{5}$          $2.75$

3. Could the area of this rectangle be 11 square units? Why or why not?

   $4\overline{)11}$
   $\underline{8}$
   $3.0$
   $2.8$
   $20$
   $20$
   $0$

   Yes because $2.75 \times 4 = 11$

## 10.2: Partitioned Rectangles When Lengths are Unknown

1. Here are two rectangles. The length and width of one rectangle are 8 and 5. The width of the other rectangle is 5, but its length is unknown so we labeled it $x$.

   Write an expression for the sum of the areas of the two rectangles.

   $x$          $8$

   $5$ | $5x$       $5$ | $40$

2. The two rectangles can be composed into one larger rectangle as shown.

   What are the width and length of the new, large rectangle?

   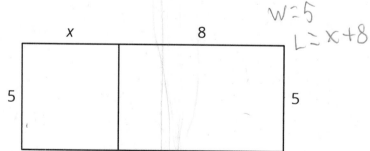

   $w = 5$
   $L = x + 8$

   $x$        $8$

   $5$                    $5$

3. Write an expression for the total area of the large rectangle as the product of its width and its length.

   $5(x + 8)$

   $5x + 40 = 45$

iM KH

# 10.3: Areas of Partitioned Rectangles

For each rectangle, write expressions for the length and width and two expressions for the total area. Record them in the table. Check your expressions in each row with your group and discuss any disagreements.

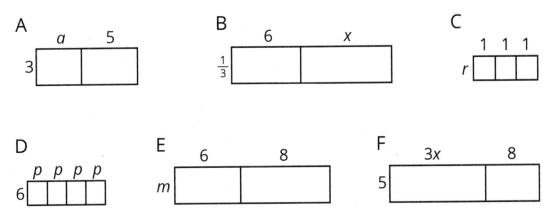

| rectangle | width | length | area as a product of width times length | area as a sum of the areas of the smaller rectangles |
|---|---|---|---|---|
| A | 3 | a+5 | 3(a+5) | 3a + 15 |
| B | $\frac{1}{3}$ | (6 ⁎ x) | $\frac{1}{3}$(6+x) | $2 + \frac{1}{3}x$ |
| C | r | 1+1+13 | r(1+1+1) | 1r+1r+1r=3r |
| D | 6 | p+p+p+p | 6(p+p+p+p) | 6p+6p+6p+6p=24p |
| E | m | 6+8 | m(6+8) | 6m+8m=14m |
| F | 5 | 3x+8 | 5(3x+8) | 15x+40 |

## Are you ready for more?

Here is an area diagram of a rectangle.

| | $y$ | $z$ |
|---|---|---|
| $w$ | $A$ | 24 |
| $x$ | 18 | 72 |

1. Find the lengths $w$, $x$, $y$, and $z$, and the area $A$. All values are whole numbers.

2. Can you find another set of lengths that will work? How many possibilities are there?

## Lesson 10 Summary

Here is a rectangle composed of two smaller rectangles A and B.

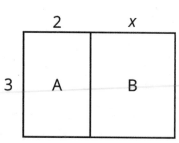

Based on the drawing, we can make several observations about the area of the rectangle:

- One side length of the large rectangle is 3 and the other is $2 + x$, so its area is $3(2 + x)$.

- Since the large rectangle can be decomposed into two smaller rectangles, A and B, with no overlap, the area of the large rectangle is also the sum of the areas of rectangles A and B: $3(2) + 3(x)$ or $6 + 3x$.

- Since both expressions represent the area of the large rectangle, they are equivalent to each other. $3(2 + x)$ is equivalent to $6 + 3x$.

We can see that multiplying 3 by the sum $2 + x$ is equivalent to multiplying 3 by 2 and then 3 by $x$ and adding the two products. This relationship is an example of the *distributive property*.

$$3(2 + x) = 3 \cdot 2 + 3 \cdot x$$

iM KH

# Lesson 10 Practice Problems

1. Here is a rectangle.

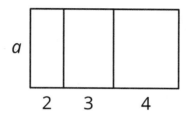

a. Explain why the area of the large rectangle is $2a + 3a + 4a$.

b. Explain why the area of the large rectangle is $(2 + 3 + 4)a$.

2. Is the area of the shaded rectangle $6(2 - m)$ or $6(m - 2)$?

Explain how you know.

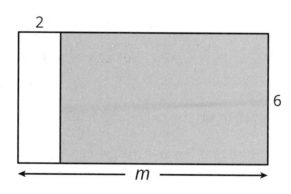

3. Choose the expressions that do *not* represent the total area of the rectangle. Select **all** that apply.

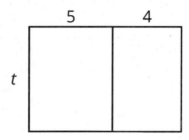

A. $5t + 4t$

B. $t + 5 + 4$

C. $9t$

D. $4 \cdot 5 \cdot t$

E. $t(5 + 4)$

4. Evaluate each expression mentally.

a. $35 \cdot 91 - 35 \cdot 89$

b. $22 \cdot 87 + 22 \cdot 13$

c. $\frac{9}{11} \cdot \frac{7}{10} - \frac{9}{11} \cdot \frac{3}{10}$

(From Unit 6, Lesson 9.)

5. Select **all** the expressions that are equivalent to $4b$.

A. $b + b + b + b$

B. $b + 4$

C. $2b + 2b$

D. $b \cdot b \cdot b \cdot b$

E. $b \div \frac{1}{4}$

(From Unit 6, Lesson 8.)

iM KH

6. Solve each equation. Show your reasoning.

$$111 = 14a \qquad\qquad 13.65 = b + 4.88 \qquad\qquad c + \frac{1}{3} = 5\frac{1}{8}$$

$$\frac{2}{5}d = \frac{17}{4} \qquad\qquad\qquad 5.16 = 4e$$

(From Unit 6, Lesson 4.)

7. Andre ran $5\frac{1}{2}$ laps of a track in 8 minutes at a constant speed. It took Andre $x$ minutes to run each lap. Select **all** the equations that represent this situation.

A. $\left(5\frac{1}{2}\right) x = 8$

B. $5\frac{1}{2} + x = 8$

C. $5\frac{1}{2} - x = 8$

D. $5\frac{1}{2} \div x = 8$

E. $x = 8 \div \left(5\frac{1}{2}\right)$

F. $x = \left(5\frac{1}{2}\right) \div 8$

(From Unit 6, Lesson 2.)

# Lesson 11: The Distributive Property, Part 3

Let's practice writing equivalent expressions by using the distributive property.

## 11.1: The Shaded Region

A rectangle with dimensions 6 cm and $w$ cm is partitioned into two smaller rectangles.

Explain why each of these expressions represents the area, in cm$^2$, of the shaded region.

- $6w - 24$

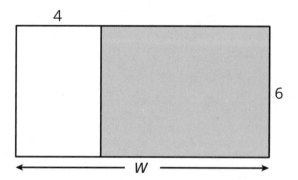

- $6(w - 4)$

## 11.2: Matching to Practice Distributive Property

Match each expression in column 1 to an equivalent expression in column 2. If you get stuck, consider drawing a diagram.

Column 1

1. $a(1 + 2 + 3)$
2. $2(12 - 4)$ $16$
3. $12a + 3b$
4. $\frac{2}{3}(15a - 18)$
5. $6a + 10b$
6. $0.4(5 - 2.5a)$
7. $2a + 3a = 5a$

Column 2

- $3(4a + b)$
- $12 \cdot 2 - 4 \cdot 2$ $16$
- $2(3a + 5b)$
- $(2 + 3)a$ $5a$
- $a + 2a + 3a$
- $10a - 12$
- $2 - a$

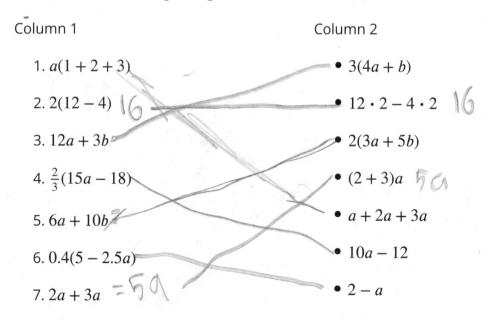

iM KH

# 11.3: Writing Equivalent Expressions Using the Distributive Property

The distributive property can be used to write equivalent expressions. In each row, use the distributive property to write an equivalent expression. If you get stuck, consider drawing a diagram.

| product | sum or difference |
|---|---|
| $3(3 + x)$ | $9 + 3x$ |
| $4(1-5)$ | $4x - 20$ |
| $(9 - 5)x$ | $9x - 5x = 4$ |
| $x(4+7)$ | $4x + 7x$ |
| $3(2x + 1)$ | $6x + 34$ |
| $5(2-1)$ | $10x - 5$ |
| $x(1+2+3)$ | $x + 2x + 3x$ |
| $\frac{1}{2}(x - 6)$ | $\frac{1}{2}x - 3$ |
| $y(3x + 4z)$ | $3yx + 4zy$ |
| $z(2xy - 3y + z)$ | $2xyz - 3yz + 4xz$ |

$\frac{1}{2} \times \frac{6}{1} = \frac{3}{1}$

$z(2xy - 3y + 4x)$

## Are you ready for more?

This rectangle has been cut up into squares of varying sizes. Both small squares have side length 1 unit. The square in the middle has side length $x$ units.

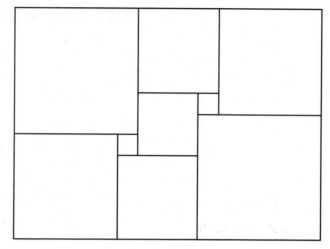

1. Suppose that $x$ is 3. Find the area of each square in the diagram. Then find the area of the large rectangle.

2. Find the side lengths of the large rectangle assuming that $x$ is 3. Find the area of the large rectangle by multiplying the length times the width. Check that this is the same area you found before.

3. Now suppose that we do not know the value of $x$. Write an expression for the side lengths of the large rectangle that involves $x$.

## Lesson 11 Summary

The distributive property can be used to write a sum as a product, or write a product as a sum. You can always draw a partitioned rectangle to help reason about it, but with enough practice, you should be able to apply the distributive property without making a drawing.

Here are some examples of expressions that are equivalent due to the distributive property.

$$9 + 18 = 9(1 + 2)$$
$$2(3x + 4) = 6x + 8$$
$$2n + 3n + n = n(2 + 3 + 1)$$
$$11b - 99a = 11(b - 9a)$$
$$k(c + d - e) = kc + kd - ke$$

iM KH

# Lesson 11 Practice Problems

1. For each expression, use the distributive property to write an equivalent expression.

    a. $4(x + 2)$

    b. $(6 + 8) \cdot x$

    c. $4(2x + 3)$

    d. $6(x + y + z)$

2. Priya rewrites the expression $8y - 24$ as $8(y - 3)$. Han rewrites $8y - 24$ as $2(4y - 12)$. Are Priya's and Han's expressions each equivalent to $8y - 24$? Explain your reasoning.

3. Select **all** the expressions that are equivalent to $16x + 36$.

    A. $16(x + 20)$

    B. $x(16 + 36)$

    C. $4(4x + 9)$

    D. $2(8x + 18)$

    E. $2(8x + 36)$

4. The area of a rectangle is $30 + 12x$. List at least 3 possibilities for the length and width of the rectangle.

5. Select **all** the expressions that are equivalent to $\frac{1}{2}z$.

    A. $z + z$

    B. $z \div 2$

    C. $z \cdot z$

    D. $\frac{1}{4}z + \frac{1}{4}z$

    E. $2z$

(From Unit 6, Lesson 8.)

6.    a. What is the perimeter of a square with side length:

    3 cm?                    7 cm?                 $s$ cm?

   b. If the perimeter of a square is 360 cm, what is its side length?

   c. What is the area of a square with side length:

    3 cm?                    7 cm?                 $s$ cm?

   d. If the area of a square is 121 cm$^2$, what is its side length?

(From Unit 6, Lesson 6.)

7. Solve each equation.

   $10 = 4a$                 $5b = 17.5$                $1.036 = 10c$

                        $0.6d = 1.8$                $15 = 0.1e$

(From Unit 6, Lesson 5.)

iM KH

# Lesson 12: Meaning of Exponents

Let's see how exponents show repeated multiplication.

## 12.1: Notice and Wonder: Dots and Lines

What do you notice? What do you wonder?

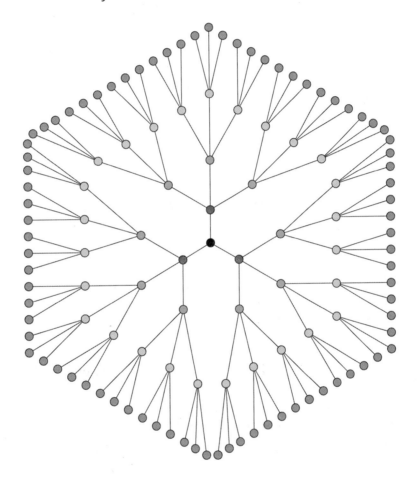

## 12.2: The Genie's Offer

You find a brass bottle that looks really old. When you rub some dirt off of the bottle, a genie appears! The genie offers you a reward. You must choose one:

$50,000 or a magical $1 coin.

The coin will turn into two coins on the first day. The two coins will turn into four coins on the second day. The four coins will double to 8 coins on the third day. The genie explains the doubling will continue for 28 days.

1. The number of coins on the third day will be $2 \cdot 2 \cdot 2$. Write an equivalent expression using exponents.

   $2^3$

2. What do $2^5$ and $2^6$ represent in this situation? Evaluate $2^5$ and $2^6$ without a calculator. Pause for discussion.

   $2^5 = 5$ days
   $2^6 = 6$ days

3. How many days would it take for the number of magical coins to exceed $50,000?

   16

4. Will the value of the magical coins exceed a million dollars within the 28 days? Explain or show your reasoning.

iM KH

**Are you ready for more?**

A scientist is growing a colony of bacteria in a petri dish. She knows that the bacteria are growing and that the number of bacteria doubles every hour.

When she leaves the lab at 5 p.m., there are 100 bacteria in the dish. When she comes back the next morning at 9 a.m., the dish is completely full of bacteria. At what time was the dish half full?

## 12.3: Make 81

1. Here are some expressions. All but one of them equals 16. Find the one that is *not* equal to 16 and explain how you know.

$$2^3 \cdot 2 \qquad\qquad 4^2 \qquad\qquad \frac{2^5}{2} \qquad\qquad 8^2$$

2. Write three expressions containing exponents so that each expression equals 81.

**Lesson 12 Summary**

When we write an expression like $2^n$, we call $n$ the exponent.

If $n$ is a positive whole number, it tells how many factors of 2 we should multiply to find the value of the expression. For example, $2^1 = 2$, and $2^5 = 2 \cdot 2 \cdot 2 \cdot 2 \cdot 2$.

There are different ways to say $2^5$. We can say "two raised to the power of five" or "two to the fifth power" or just "two to the fifth."

# Lesson 12 Practice Problems

1. Select **all** the expressions that are equivalent to 64.

   A. $2^6$

   B. $2^8$

   C. $4^3$

   D. $8^2$

   E. $16^4$

   F. $32^2$

2. Select **all** the expressions that equal $3^4$.

   A. 7

   B. $4^3$

   C. 12

   D. 81

   E. 64

   F. $9^2$

3. $4^5$ is equal to 1,024. Evaluate each expression.

   a. $4^6$

   b. $4^4$

   c. $4^3 \cdot 4^2$

4. $6^3 = 216$. Using exponents, write three more expressions whose value is 216.

5. Find two different ways to rewrite $3xy + 6yz$ using the distributive property.

(From Unit 6, Lesson 11.)

6. Solve each equation.

$a - 2.01 = 5.5$                      $b + 2.01 = 5.5$

$10c = 13.71$                      $100d = 13.71$

(From Unit 6, Lesson 5.)

7. Which expressions represent the total area of the large rectangle? Select **all** that apply.

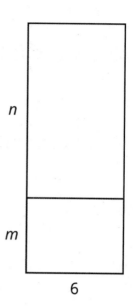

A. $6(m + n)$

B. $6n + m$

C. $6n + 6m$

D. $6mn$

E. $(n + m)6$

(From Unit 6, Lesson 10.)

8. Is each statement true or false? Explain your reasoning.

a. $\frac{45}{100} \cdot 72 = \frac{45}{72} \cdot 100$

b. 16% of 250 is equal to 250% of 16

(From Unit 3, Lesson 16.)

iM KH

# Lesson 13: Expressions with Exponents

Let's use the meaning of exponents to decide if equations are true.

## 13.1: Which One Doesn't Belong: Twos

Which one doesn't belong?

$2 \cdot 2 \cdot 2 \cdot 2$                                     $2^4$

$16$                                                     $4 \cdot 2$

## 13.2: Is the Equation True?

Decide whether each equation is true or false, and explain how you know.

1. $2^4 = 2 \cdot 4$

2. $3 + 3 + 3 + 3 + 3 = 3^5$

3. $5^3 = 5 \cdot 5 \cdot 5$

4. $2^3 = 3^2$

5. $16^1 = 8^2$

6. $\frac{1}{2} \cdot \frac{1}{2} \cdot \frac{1}{2} \cdot \frac{1}{2} = 4 \cdot \frac{1}{2}$

7. $\left(\frac{1}{2}\right)^4 = \frac{1}{8}$

8. $8^2 = 4^3$

# 13.3: What's Your Reason?

In each list, find expressions that are equivalent to each other and explain to your partner why they are equivalent. Your partner listens to your explanation. If you disagree, explain your reasoning until you agree. Switch roles for each list. (There may be more than two equivalent expressions in each list.)

1. a. $5 \cdot 5$

   b. $2^5$

   c. $5^2$

   d. $2 \cdot 5$

2. a. $4^3$

   b. $3^4$

   c. $4 \cdot 4 \cdot 4$

   d. $4 + 4 + 4$

3. a. $6 + 6 + 6$

   b. $6^3$

   c. $3^6$

   d. $3 \cdot 6$

4. a. $11^5$

   b. $11 \cdot 11 \cdot 11 \cdot 11 \cdot 11$

   c. $11 \cdot 5$

   d. $5^{11}$

iM KH

5.  a. $\frac{1}{5} \cdot \frac{1}{5} \cdot \frac{1}{5}$

    b. $\left(\frac{1}{5}\right)^3$

    c. $\frac{1}{15}$

    d. $\frac{1}{125}$

6.  a. $\left(\frac{5}{3}\right)^2$

    b. $\left(\frac{3}{5}\right)^2$

    c. $\frac{10}{6}$

    d. $\frac{25}{9}$

## Are you ready for more?

What is the last digit of $3^{1,000}$? Show or explain your reasoning.

## Lesson 13 Summary

When working with exponents, the bases don't have to always be whole numbers. They can also be other kinds of numbers, like fractions, decimals, and even variables. For example, we can use exponents in each of the following ways:

$$\left(\frac{2}{3}\right)^4 = \frac{2}{3} \cdot \frac{2}{3} \cdot \frac{2}{3} \cdot \frac{2}{3}$$

$$(1.7)^3 = (1.7) \cdot (1.7) \cdot (1.7)$$

$$x^5 = x \cdot x \cdot x \cdot x \cdot x$$

# Lesson 13 Practice Problems

1. Select **all** expressions that are equal to $3 \cdot 3 \cdot 3 \cdot 3 \cdot 3$.

   A. $3 \cdot 5$

   B. $3^5$

   C. $3^4 \cdot 3$

   D. $5 \cdot 3$

   E. $5^3$

2. Noah starts with 0 and then adds the number 5 four times. Diego starts with 1 and then multiplies by the number 5 four times. For each expression, decide whether it is equal to Noah's result, Diego's result, or neither.

   a. $4 \cdot 5$

   b. $4 + 5$

   c. $4^5$

   d. $5^4$

3. Decide whether each equation is true or false, and explain how you know.

   a. $9 \cdot 9 \cdot 3 = 3^5$

   b. $7 + 7 + 7 = 3 + 3 + 3 + 3 + 3 + 3 + 3$

   c. $\frac{1}{7} \cdot \frac{1}{7} \cdot \frac{1}{7} = \frac{3}{7}$

   d. $4^1 = 4 \cdot 1$

   e. $6 + 6 + 6 = 6^3$

iM KH

4.   a. What is the area of a square with side lengths of $\frac{3}{5}$ units?

b. What is the side length of a square with area $\frac{1}{16}$ square units?

c. What is the volume of a cube with edge lengths of $\frac{2}{3}$ units?

d. What is the edge length of a cube with volume $\frac{27}{64}$ cubic units?

5. Select **all** the expressions that represent the area of the shaded rectangle.

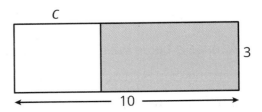

A. $3(10 - c)$

B. $3(c - 10)$

C. $10(c - 3)$

D. $10(3 - c)$

E. $30 - 3c$

F. $30 - 10c$

(From Unit 6, Lesson 10.)

6. A ticket at a movie theater costs $8.50. One night, the theater had $29,886 in ticket sales.

  a. Estimate about how many tickets the theater sold. Explain your reasoning.

  b. How many tickets did the theater sell? Explain your reasoning.

(From Unit 5, Lesson 13.)

7. A fence is being built around a rectangular garden that is $8\frac{1}{2}$ feet by $6\frac{1}{3}$ feet. Fencing comes in panels. Each panel is $\frac{2}{3}$ of a foot wide. How many panels are needed? Explain or show your reasoning.

(From Unit 4, Lesson 12.)

302

iM KH

# Lesson 14: Evaluating Expressions with Exponents

Let's find the values of expressions with exponents.

## 14.1: Revisiting the Cube

Based on the given information, what other measurements of the square and cube could we find?

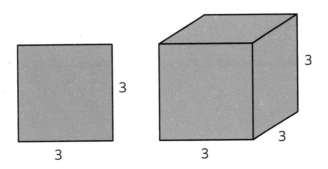

## 14.2: Calculating Surface Area

A cube has side length 10 inches. Jada says the surface area of the cube is 600 in$^2$, and Noah says the surface area of the cube is 3,600 in$^2$. Here is how each of them reasoned:

Jada's Method:

$6 \cdot 10^2$
$6 \cdot 100$
$600$

Noah's Method:

$6 \cdot 10^2$
$60^2$
$3,600$

Do you agree with either of them? Explain your reasoning.

# 14.3: Row Game: Expression Explosion

Evaluate the expressions in one of the columns. Your partner will work on the other column. Check with your partner after you finish each row. Your answers in each row should be the same. If your answers aren't the same, work together to find the error.

| column A | column B |
|---|---|
| $5^2 + 4$ | $2^2 + 25$ |
| $2^4 \cdot 5$ | $2^3 \cdot 10$ |
| $3 \cdot 4^2$ | $12 \cdot 2^2$ |
| $20 + 2^3$ | $1 + 3^3$ |
| $9 \cdot 2^1$ | $3 \cdot 6^1$ |
| $\frac{1}{9} \cdot \left(\frac{1}{2}\right)^3$ | $\frac{1}{8} \cdot \left(\frac{1}{3}\right)^2$ |

$$\frac{1}{9} \times \frac{1}{8} = \frac{1}{72}$$

## Are you ready for more?

1. Consider this equation: $\square^2 + \square^2 = \square^2$. An example of 3 different whole numbers that could go in the boxes are 3, 4, and 5, since $3^2 + 4^2 = 5^2$. (That is, $9 + 16 = 25$.)

   Can you find a different set of 3 whole numbers that make the equation true?

2. How many sets of 3 different whole numbers can you find?

iM KH

3. Can you find a set of 3 different whole numbers that make this equation true?

$$\square^3 + \square^3 = \square^3$$

4. How about this one? $\square^4 + \square^4 = \square^4$

Once you have worked on this a little while, you can understand a problem that is famous in the history of math. (Alas, this space is too small to contain it.) If you are interested, consider doing some further research on *Fermat's Last Theorem*.

## Lesson 14 Summary

Exponents give us a new way to describe operations with numbers, so we need to understand how exponents get along with the other operations we know.

When we write $6 \cdot 4^2$, we want to make sure everyone agrees about how to evaluate this. Otherwise some people might multiply first and others compute the exponent first, and different people would get different values for the same expression!

Earlier we saw situations in which $6 \cdot 4^2$ represented the surface area of a cube with side lengths 4 units. When computing the surface area, we evaluate $4^2$ first (or find the area of one face of the cube first) and then multiply the result by 6. In many other expressions that use exponents, the part with an exponent is intended to be evaluated first.

To make everyone agree about the value of expressions like $6 \cdot 4^2$, the convention is to *evaluate the part of the expression with the exponent first*. Here are a couple of examples:

$$6 \cdot 4^2$$
$$6 \cdot 16$$
$$96$$

$$45 + 5^2$$
$$45 + 25$$
$$70$$

If we want to communicate that 6 and 4 should be multiplied first and then squared, then we can use parentheses to group parts together:

$$(6 \cdot 4)^2$$
$$24^2$$
$$576$$

$$(45 + 5)^2$$
$$50^2$$
$$2,500$$

# Lesson 14 Practice Problems

1. Lin says, "I took the number 8, and then multiplied it by the square of 3." Select **all** the expressions that equal Lin's answer.

   A. $8 \cdot 3^2$

   B. $(8 \cdot 3)^2$

   C. $8 \cdot 2^3$

   D. $3^2 \cdot 8$

   E. $24^2$

   F. 72

2. Evaluate each expression.

   a. $7 + 2^3 = 15$

   b. $9 \cdot 3^1 = 27$

   c. $20 - 2^4 = 4$

   d. $2 \cdot 6^2 = 72$

   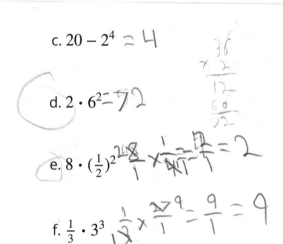

   e. $8 \cdot (\frac{1}{2})^2 = 2$

   f. $\frac{1}{3} \cdot 3^3 = 9$

   g. $(\frac{1}{5} \cdot 5)^5 = 1$

3. Andre says, "I multiplied 4 by 5, then cubed the result." Select **all** the expressions that equal Andre's answer.

    A. $4 \cdot 5^3$

    B. $(4 \cdot 5)^3$

    C. $(4 \cdot 5)^2$

    D. $5^3 \cdot 4$

    E. $20^3$

    F. 500

    G. 8,000

4. Han has 10 cubes, each 5 inches on a side.

    a. Find the total volume of Han's cubes. Express your answer as an expression using an exponent.

    b. Find the total surface area of Han's cubes. Express your answer as an expression using an exponent.

5. Priya says that $\frac{1}{3} \cdot \frac{1}{3} \cdot \frac{1}{3} \cdot \frac{1}{3} = \frac{4}{3}$. Do you agree with Priya? Explain or show your reasoning.

    (From Unit 6, Lesson 13.)

6. Answer each question. Show your reasoning.

    a. 125% of $e$ is 30. What is $e$?

    b. 35% of $f$ is 14. What is $f$?

    (From Unit 6, Lesson 7.)

7. Which expressions are solutions to the equation $2.4y = 13.75$? Select **all** that apply.

    A. $13.75 - 1.4$

    B. $13.75 \cdot 2.4$

    C. $13.75 \div 2.4$

    D. $\frac{13.75}{2.4}$

    E. $2.4 \div 13.75$

    (From Unit 6, Lesson 5.)

8. Jada explains how she finds $15 \cdot 23$:

    "I know that ten 23s is 230, so five 23s will be half of 230, which is 115. 15 is 10 plus 5, so $15 \cdot 23$ is 230 plus 115, which is 345."

    a. Do you agree with Jada? Explain.

    b. Draw a 15 by 23 rectangle. Partition the rectangle into two rectangles and label them to show Jada's reasoning.

    (From Unit 5, Lesson 7.)

iM KH

# Lesson 15: Equivalent Exponential Expressions

Let's investigate expressions with variables and exponents.

## 15.1: Up or Down?

Find the values of $3^x$ and $\left(\frac{1}{3}\right)^x$ for different values of $x$. What patterns do you notice?

| $x$ | $3^x$ | $\left(\frac{1}{3}\right)^x$ |
|-----|-------|------------------------------|
| 1   |       |                              |
| 2   |       |                              |
| 3   |       |                              |
| 4   |       |                              |

## 15.2: What's the Value?

Evaluate each expression for the given value of $x$.

1. $3x^2$ when $x$ is 10 $= 300$

2. $3x^2$ when $x$ is $\frac{1}{9}$ $\quad \frac{3}{1} \times \frac{1}{81} = \frac{3}{81}$

3. $\frac{x^3}{4}$ when $x$ is 4 $\quad = 64 \div 4 = 16$

4. $\frac{x^3}{4}$ when $x$ is $\frac{1}{2}$ $= \frac{1}{8} \times \frac{1}{4} = \frac{1}{32}$

5. $9 + x^7$ when $x$ is 1 $= 10$

6. $9 + x^7$ when $x$ is $\frac{1}{2}$ $\quad \frac{1}{128} + \frac{9}{1} = \frac{9}{128}$

## 15.3: Exponent Experimentation

Find a solution to each equation in the list. (Numbers in the list may be a solution to more than one equation, and not all numbers in the list will be used.)

1. $64 = x^2$

2. $64 = x^3$

3. $2^x = 32$

4. $x = \left(\frac{2}{5}\right)^3$

5. $\frac{16}{9} = x^2$

6. $2 \cdot 2^5 = 2^x$

7. $2x = 2^4$

8. $4^3 = 8^x$

List:

$\frac{8}{125}$    $\frac{6}{15}$    $\frac{5}{8}$    $\frac{8}{9}$    1    $\frac{4}{3}$    2    3    4    5    6    8

### Are you ready for more?

This fractal is called a Sierpinski Tetrahedron. A tetrahedron is a polyhedron that has four faces. (The plural of tetrahedron is tetrahedra.)

The small tetrahedra form four medium-sized tetrahedra: blue, red, yellow, and green. The medium-sized tetrahedra form one large tetrahedron.

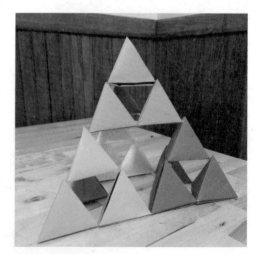

1. How many small faces does this fractal have? Be sure to include faces you can't see. Try to find a way to figure this out so that you don't have to count every face.

iM KH

2. How many small tetrahedra are in the bottom layer, touching the table?

3. To make an even bigger version of this fractal, you could take four fractals like the one pictured and put them together. Explain where you would attach the fractals to make a bigger tetrahedron.

4. How many small faces would this bigger fractal have? How many small tetrahedra would be in the bottom layer?

5. What other patterns can you find?

## Lesson 15 Summary

In this lesson, we saw expressions that used the letter $x$ as a variable. We evaluated these expressions for different values of $x$.

- To evaluate the expression $2x^3$ when $x$ is 5, we replace the letter $x$ with 5 to get $2 \cdot 5^3$. This is equal to $2 \cdot 125$ or just 250. So the value of $2x^3$ is 250 when $x$ is 5.

- To evaluate $\frac{x^2}{8}$ when $x$ is 4, we replace the letter $x$ with 4 to get $\frac{4^2}{8} = \frac{16}{8}$, which equals 2. So $\frac{x^2}{8}$ has a value of 2 when $x$ is 4.

We also saw equations with the variable $x$ and had to decide what value of $x$ would make the equation true.

- Suppose we have an equation $10 \cdot 3^x = 90$ and a list of possible solutions: $1, 2, 3, 9, 11$. The only value of $x$ that makes the equation true is 2 because $10 \cdot 3^2 = 10 \cdot 3 \cdot 3$, which equals 90. So 2 is the solution to the equation.

# Lesson 15 Practice Problems

1. Evaluate each expression if $x = 3$.

   a. $2^x = 8$

   b. $x^2 = 9$

   c. $1^x = 1$

   d. $x^1 = 3$

   e. $\left(\frac{1}{2}\right)^x = \frac{1}{8}$

2. Evaluate each expression for the given value of each variable.

   a. $2 + x^3$, $x$ is 3 $= 29$

   b. $x^2$, $x$ is $\frac{1}{2}$ $= \frac{1}{4}$

   c. $3x^2 + y$, $x$ is 5 $y$ is 3

   $65 + 3 = 68$

   $$\begin{array}{r} 25 \\ \times\ 3 \\ \hline 15 \\ 60 \\ \hline 65 \end{array}$$

   d. $10y + x^2$, $x$ is 6 $y$ is 4

   $40 + 36 = 76$

3. Decide if the expressions have the same value. If not, determine which expression has the larger value.

   a. $2^3$ and $3^2$

   b. $1^{31}$ and $31^1$

   c. $4^2$ and $2^4$

   d. $\left(\frac{1}{2}\right)^3$ and $\left(\frac{1}{3}\right)^2$

iM KH

4. Match each equation to its solution.

A. $7 + x^2 = 16$

B. $5 - x^2 = 1$

C. $2 \cdot 2^3 = 2^x$

D. $\frac{3^4}{3^x} = 27$

1. $x = 1$

2. $x = 2$

3. $x = 3$

4. $x = 4$

5. An adult pass at the amusement park costs 1.6 times as much as a child's pass.

   a. How many dollars does an adult pass cost if a child's pass costs:

   $5?                    $10?                    $w$ dollars?

   b. A child's pass costs $15. How many dollars does an adult pass cost?

   (From Unit 6, Lesson 6.)

6. Jada reads 5 pages every 20 minutes. At this rate, how many pages can she read in 1 hour?

   ○ Use a double number line to find the answer.

   ○ Use a table to find the answer.

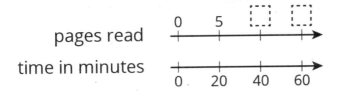

| pages read | time in minutes |
|---|---|
| 5 | 20 |
|  |  |
|  |  |

   Which strategy do you think is better, and why?

   (From Unit 2, Lesson 14.)

# Lesson 16: Two Related Quantities, Part 1

Let's use equations and graphs to describe relationships with ratios.

## 16.1: Which One Would You Choose?

Which one would you choose? Be prepared to explain your reasoning.

- A 5-pound jug of honey for $15.35

- Three 1.5-pound jars of honey for $13.05

iM KH

## 16.2: Painting the Set

Lin needs to mix a specific shade of orange paint for the set of the school play. The color uses 3 parts yellow for every 2 parts red.

1. Complete the table to show different combinations of red and yellow paint that will make the shade of orange Lin needs.

| cups of red paint ($r$) | cups of yellow paint ($y$) | total cups of paint ($t$) |
|---|---|---|
| 2 | 3 | |
| 6 | | |
| | | 20 |
| | 18 | |
| 14 | | |
| 16 | | |
| | | 50 |
| | 42 | |

2. Lin notices that the number of cups of red paint is always $\frac{2}{5}$ of the total number of cups. She writes the equation $r = \frac{2}{5}t$ to describe the relationship. Which is the **independent variable**? Which is the **dependent variable**? Explain how you know.

3. Write an equation that describes the relationship between $r$ and $y$ where $y$ is the independent variable.

4. Write an equation that describes the relationship between $y$ and $r$ where $r$ is the independent variable.

5. Use the points in the table to create two graphs that show the relationship between $r$ and $y$. Match each relationship to one of the equations you wrote.

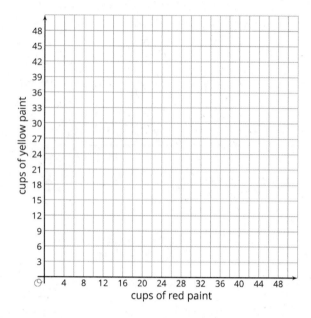

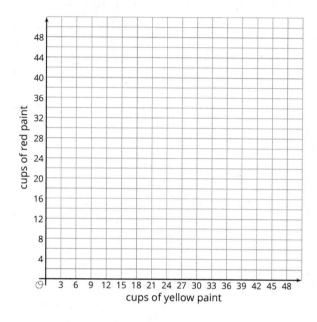

## Are you ready for more?

A fruit stand sells apples, peaches, and tomatoes. Today, they sold 4 apples for every 5 peaches. They sold 2 peaches for every 3 tomatoes. They sold 132 pieces of fruit in total. How many of each fruit did they sell?

## Lesson 16 Summary

Equations are very useful for describing sets of equivalent ratios. Here is an example.

A pie recipe calls for 3 green apples for every 5 red apples. We can create a table to show some equivalent ratios.

We can see from the table that $r$ is always $\frac{5}{3}$ as large as $g$ and that $g$ is always $\frac{3}{5}$ as large as $r$.

| green apples ($g$) | red apples ($r$) |
|---|---|
| 3 | 5 |
| 6 | 10 |
| 9 | 15 |
| 12 | 20 |

iM KH

We can write equations to describe the relationship between $g$ and $r$.

- When we know the number of green apples and want to find the number of red apples, we can write:

$$r = \frac{5}{3}g$$

  In this equation, if $g$ changes, $r$ is affected by the change, so we refer to $g$ as the **independent variable** and $r$ as the **dependent variable**.

  We can use this equation with any value of $g$ to find $r$. If 270 green apples are used, then $\frac{5}{3} \cdot (270)$ or 450 red apples are used.

- When we know the number of red apples and want to find the number of green apples, we can write:

$$g = \frac{3}{5}r$$

  In this equation, if $r$ changes, $g$ is affected by the change, so we refer to $r$ as the independent variable and $g$ as the dependent variable.

  We can use this equation with any value of $r$ to find $g$. If 275 red apples are used, then $\frac{3}{5} \cdot (275)$ or 165 green apples are used.

We can also graph the two equations we wrote to get a visual picture of the relationship between the two quantities.

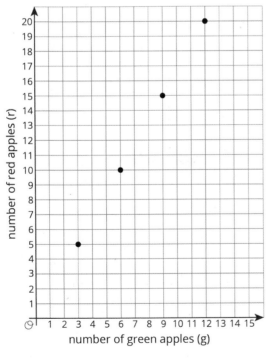

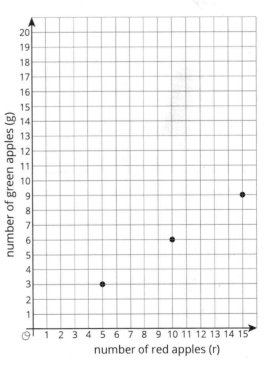

## Glossary

- dependent variable
- independent variable

# Lesson 16 Practice Problems

1. Here is a graph that shows some values for the number of cups of sugar, $s$, required to make $x$ batches of brownies.

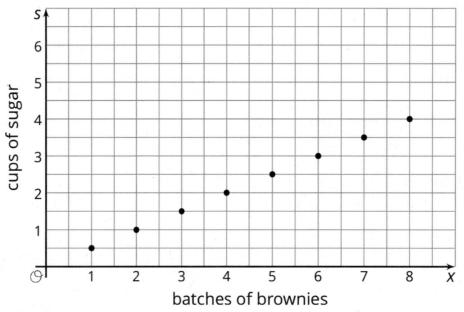

   a. Complete the table so that the pair of numbers in each column represents the coordinates of a point on the graph.

| $x$ | 1 | 2 | 3 | 4 | 5 | 6 | 7 |
|-----|---|---|---|---|---|---|---|
| $s$ |   |   |   |   |   |   |   |

   b. What does the point $(8, 4)$ mean in terms of the amount of sugar and number of batches of brownies?

   c. Write an equation that shows the amount of sugar in terms of the number of batches.

2. Each serving of a certain fruit snack contains 90 calories.

   a. Han wants to know how many calories he gets from the fruit snacks. Write an equation that shows the number of calories, $c$, in terms of the number of servings, $n$.

   b. Tyler needs some extra calories each day during his sports season. He wants to know how many servings he can have each day if all the extra calories come from the fruit snack. Write an equation that shows the number of servings, $n$, in terms of the number of calories, $c$.

3. Kiran shops for books during a 20% off sale.

   a. What percent of the original price of a book does Kiran pay during the sale?

   b. Complete the table to show how much Kiran pays for books during the sale.

   c. Write an equation that relates the sale price, $s$, to the original price $p$.

   d. On graph paper, create a graph showing the relationship between the sale price and the original price by plotting the points from the table.

| original price in dollars ($p$) | sale price in dollars ($s$) |
|---|---|
| 1 | |
| 2 | |
| 3 | |
| 4 | |
| 5 | |
| 6 | |
| 7 | |
| 8 | |
| 9 | |
| 10 | |

4. Evaluate each expression when $x$ is 4 and $y$ is 6.

    a. $(6 - x)^3 + y$

    b. $2 + x^3$

    c. $2^x - 2y$

    d. $\left(\frac{1}{2}\right)^x$

    e. $1^x + 2^x$

    f. $\frac{2^x}{x^2}$

(From Unit 6, Lesson 15.)

5. Find $(12.34) \cdot (0.7)$. Show your reasoning.

(From Unit 5, Lesson 8.)

6. For each expression, write another division expression that has the same value and that can be used to help find the quotient. Then, find each quotient.

    a. $302.1 \div 0.5$

    b. $12.15 \div 0.02$

    c. $1.375 \div 0.11$

(From Unit 5, Lesson 13.)

iM KH

# Lesson 17: Two Related Quantities, Part 2

Let's use equations and graphs to describe stories with constant speed.

## 17.1: Walking to the Library

Lin and Jada each walk at a steady rate from school to the library. Lin can walk 13 miles in 5 hours, and Jada can walk 25 miles in 10 hours. They each leave school at 3:00 and walk $3\frac{1}{4}$ miles to the library. What time do they each arrive?

## 17.2: The Walk-a-thon

Diego, Elena, and Andre participated in a walk-a-thon to raise money for cancer research. They each walked at a constant rate, but their rates were different.

1. Complete the table to show how far each participant walked during the walk-a-thon.

| time in hours | miles walked by Diego | miles walked by Elena | miles walked by Andre |
|---|---|---|---|
| 1 | | | |
| 2 | 6 | | |
| | 12 | 11 | |
| 5 | | | 17.5 |

2. How fast was each participant walking in miles per hour?

3. How long did it take each participant to walk one mile?

4. Graph the progress of each person in the **coordinate plane**. Use a different color for each participant.

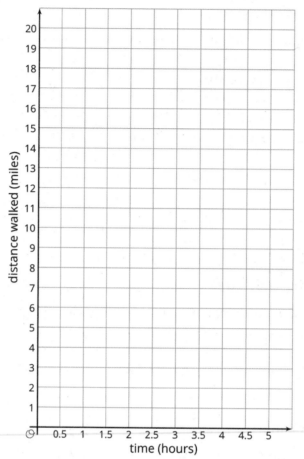

5. Diego says that $d = 3t$ represents his walk, where $d$ is the distance walked in miles and $t$ is the time in hours.

   a. Explain why $d = 3t$ relates the distance Diego walked to the time it took.

   b. Write two equations that relate distance and time: one for Elena and one for Andre.

6. Use the equations you wrote to predict how far each participant would walk, at their same rate, in 8 hours.

7. For Diego's equation and the equations you wrote, which is the dependent variable and which is the independent variable?

iM KH

## Are you ready for more?

1. Two trains are traveling toward each other, on parallel tracks. Train A is moving at a constant speed of 70 miles per hour. Train B is moving at a constant speed of 50 miles per hour. The trains are initially 320 miles apart. How long will it take them to meet? One way to start thinking about this problem is to make a table. Add as many rows as you like.

|  | train A | train B |
|---|---|---|
| starting position | 0 miles | 320 miles |
| after 1 hour | 70 miles | 270 miles |
| after 2 hours |  |  |
|  |  |  |
|  |  |  |

2. How long will it take a train traveling at 120 miles per hour to go 320 miles?

3. Explain the connection between these two problems.

## Lesson 17 Summary

Equations are very useful for solving problems with constant speeds. Here is an example.

A boat is traveling at a constant speed of 25 miles per hour.

1. How far can the boat travel in 3.25 hours?

2. How long does it take for the boat to travel 60 miles?

We can write equations to help us answer questions like these.

Let's use $t$ to represent the time in hours and $d$ to represent the distance in miles that the boat travels.

When we know the time and want to find the distance, we can write:
$$d = 25t$$

In this equation, if $t$ changes, $d$ is affected by the change, so we $t$ is the independent variable and $d$ is the dependent variable.

This equation can help us find $d$ when we have any value of $t$. In 3.25 hours, the boat can travel 25(3.25) or 81.25 miles.

When we know the distance and want to find the time, we can write:
$$t = \frac{d}{25}$$

In this equation, if $d$ changes, $t$ is affected by the change, so we $d$ is the independent variable and $t$ is the dependent variable.

This equation can help us find $t$ when for any value of $d$. To travel 60 miles, it will take $\frac{60}{25}$ or $2\frac{2}{5}$ hours.

These problems can also be solved using important ratio techniques such as a table of equivalent ratios. The equations are particularly valuable in this case because the answers are not round numbers or easy to quickly evaluate.

We can also graph the two equations we wrote to get a visual picture of the relationship between the two quantities:

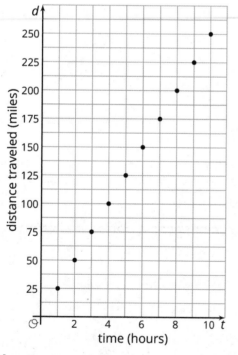

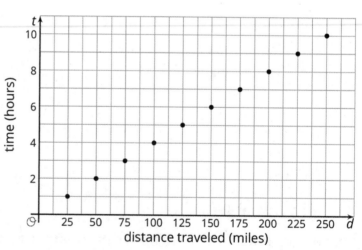

## Glossary

- coordinate plane

iM KH

# Lesson 17 Practice Problems

1. A car is traveling down a road at a constant speed of 50 miles per hour.

a. Complete the table with the amounts of time it takes the car to travel certain distances, or the distances traveled for certain amounts of time.

b. Write an equation that represents the distance traveled by the car, $d$, for an amount of time, $t$.

c. In your equation, which is the dependent variable and which is the independent variable?

| time (hours) | distance (miles) |
|---|---|
| 2 | |
| 1.5 | |
| $t$ | |
| | 50 |
| | 300 |
| | $d$ |

2. The graph represents the amount of time in hours it takes a ship to travel various distances in miles.

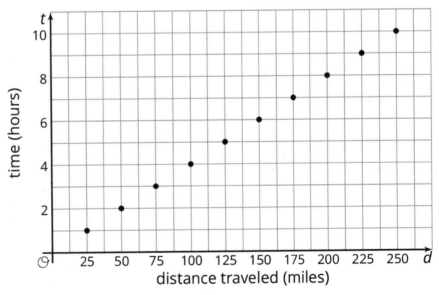

distance traveled (miles)

a. Write the coordinates of one point on the graph. What does the point represent?

b. What is the speed of the ship in miles per hour?

c. Write an equation that relates the time, $t$, it takes to travel a given distance, $d$.

3. Find a solution to each equation in the list that follows (not all numbers will be used):

a. $2^x = 8$

b. $2^x = 2$

c. $x^2 = 100$

d. $x^2 = \frac{1}{100}$

e. $x^1 = 7$

f. $2^x \cdot 2^3 = 2^7$

g. $\frac{2^x}{2^3} = 2^5$

List:    $\frac{1}{10}$    $\frac{1}{3}$    1    2    3    4    5    7    8    10    16

(From Unit 6, Lesson 15.)

iM KH

4. Select **all** the expressions that are equivalent to $5x + 30x - 15x$.

    A. $5(x + 6x - 3x)$

    B. $(5 + 30 - 15) \cdot x$

    C. $x(5 + 30x - 15x)$

    D. $5x(1 + 6 - 3)$

    E. $5(x + 30x - 15x)$

(From Unit 6, Lesson 11.)

5. Evaluate each expression if $x$ is 1, $y$ is 2, and $z$ is 3.

    a. $7x^2 - z$

    b. $(x + 4)^3 - y$

    c. $y(x + 3^3)$

    d. $(7 - y + z)^2$

    e. $0.241x + x^3$

(From Unit 6, Lesson 15.)

# Lesson 18: More Relationships

Let's use graphs and equations to show relationships involving area, volume, and exponents.

## 18.1: Which One Doesn't Belong: Graphs

Which one doesn't belong?

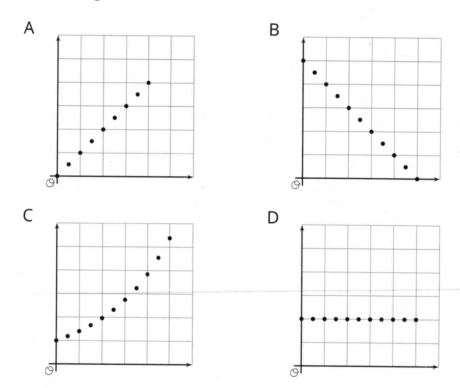

## 18.2: Making a Banner

Mai is creating a rectangular banner to advertise the school play. The material for the banner is sold by the square foot. Mai has enough money to buy 36 square feet of material. She is trying to decide on the length and width of the banner.

1. If the length is 6 feet, what is the width?

2. If the length is 4 feet, what is the width?

3. If the length is 9 feet, what is the width?

iM KH

4. To find different combinations of length and width that give an area of 36 square feet, Mai uses the equation $w = \frac{36}{\ell}$, where $w$ is the width and $\ell$ is the length. Compare your strategy and Mai's method for finding the width. How were they the same or different?

5. Use several combinations of length and width to create a graph that shows the relationship between the side lengths of various rectangles with area 36 square feet.

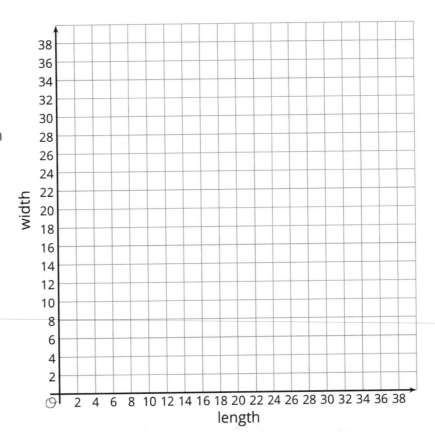

6. Explain how the graph describes the relationship between length and width for different rectangles with area 36.

7. Suppose Mai used the equation $\ell = \frac{36}{w}$ to find the length for different values of the width. Would the graph be different if she graphed length on the vertical axis and width on the horizontal axis? Explain how you know.

## 18.3: Cereal Boxes

A cereal manufacturer needs to design a cereal box that has a volume of 225 cubic inches and a height that is no more than 15 inches.

1. The designers know that the volume of a rectangular prism can be calculated by multiplying the area of its base and its height. Complete the table with pairs of values that will make the volume 225 $in^3$.

| height (in) | | 5 | 9 | 12 | | $7\frac{1}{2}$ |
|---|---|---|---|---|---|---|
| area of base ($in^2$) | 75 | | | | 15 | |

2. Describe how you found the missing values for the table.

3. Write an equation that shows how the area of the base, $A$, is affected by changes in the height, $h$, for different rectangular prisms with volume 225 $in^3$.

4. Plot the ordered pairs from the table on the graph to show the relationship between the area of the base and the height for different boxes box with volume 225 $in^3$.

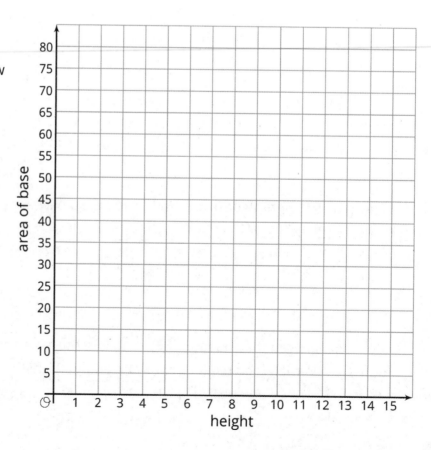

# 18.4: Multiplying Mosquitoes

A researcher who is studying mosquito populations collects the following data:

| day in the study ($d$) | number of mosquitoes ($n$) |
|---|---|
| 1 | 2 |
| 2 | 4 |
| 3 | 8 |
| 4 | 16 |
| 5 | 32 |

1. The researcher said that, for these five days, the number of mosquitoes, $n$, can be found with the equation $n = 2^d$ where $d$ is the day in the study. Explain why this equation matches the data.

2. Use the ordered pairs in the table to graph the relationship between number of mosquitoes and day in the study for these five days.

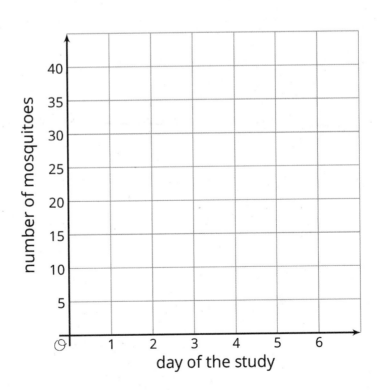

3. Describe the graph. Compare how the data, equation, and graph illustrate the relationship between the day in the study and the number of mosquitoes.

4. If the pattern continues, how many mosquitoes will there be on day 6?

## Lesson 18 Summary

Equations can represent relationships between geometric quantities. For instance:

- If $s$ is the side length of a square, then the area $A$ is related to $s$ by $A = s^2$.

- Sometimes the relationships are more specific. For example, the perimeter $P$ of a rectangle with length $l$ and width $w$ is $P = 2l + 2w$. If we consider only rectangles with a length of 10, then the relationship between the perimeter and the width is $P = 20 + 2w$.

Here is another example of an equation with exponent expressing the relationship between quantities:

- A super ball is dropped from 10 feet. On each successive bounce, it only goes $\frac{1}{2}$ as high as on the previous bounce.

  This means that on the first bounce, the ball will bounce 5 feet high, and then on the second bounce it will only go $2\frac{1}{2}$ feet high, and so on. We can represent this situation with an equation to find how high the super ball will bounce after any number of bounces.

  To find how high the super ball bounces on the $n^{\text{th}}$ bounce, we have to multiply 10 feet (the initial height) by $\frac{1}{2}$ and multiply by $\frac{1}{2}$ again for each bounce thereafter; we need to do this $n$ times. So the height, $h$, of the ball on the $n^{\text{th}}$ bounce will be $h = 10\left(\frac{1}{2}\right)^n$. In this equation, the dependent variable, $h$, is affected by changes in the independent variable, $n$.

Equations and graphs can give us insight into different kinds of relationships between quantities and help us answer questions and solve problems.

iM KH

# Lesson 18 Practice Problems

1. Elena is designing a logo in the shape of a parallelogram. She wants the logo to have an area of 12 square inches. She draws bases of different lengths and tries to compute the height for each.

    a. Write an equation Elena can use to find the height, $h$, for each value of the base, $b$.

    b. Use your equation to find the height of a parallelogram with base $1.5$ inches.

2. Han is planning to ride his bike 24 miles.

    a. How long will it take if he rides at a rate of:

    3 miles per hour?        4 miles per hour?        6 miles per hour?

    b. Write an equation that Han can use to find $t$, the time it will take to ride 24 miles, if his rate in miles per hour is represented by $r$.

    c. On graph paper, draw a graph that shows $t$ in terms of $r$ for a 24-mile ride.

3. The graph of the equation $V = 10s^3$ contains the points $(2, 80)$ and $(4, 640)$.

    a. Create a story that is represented by this graph.

    b. What do the points mean in the context of your story?

4. You find a brass bottle that looks really old. When you rub some dirt off of the bottle, a genie appears! The genie offers you a reward. You must choose one:

$50,000 or a magical $1 coin.

The coin will turn into two coins on the first day. The two coins will turn into four coins on the second day. The four coins will double to 8 coins on the third day. The genie explains the doubling will continue for 28 days.

   a. Write an equation that shows the number of coins, $n$, in terms of the day, $d$.

   b. Create a table that shows the number of coins for each day for the first 15 days.

   c. Create a graph for days 7 through 12 that shows how the number of coins grows with each day.

5. At a market, 3.1 pounds of peaches cost $7.72. How much did the peaches cost per pound? Explain or show your reasoning. Round your answer to the nearest cent.

(From Unit 5, Lesson 13.)

6. Andre set up a lemonade stand last weekend. It cost him $0.15 to make each cup of lemonade, and he sold each cup for $0.35.

   a. If Andre collects $9.80, how many cups did he sell?

   b. How much money did it cost Andre to make this amount of lemonade?

   c. How much money did Andre make in profit?

(From Unit 5, Lesson 13.)

# Lesson 19: Tables, Equations, and Graphs, Oh My!

- Let's explore some equations from real-world situations.

## 19.1: Matching Equations and Tables

Match each equation with a table that represents the same relationship. Be prepared to explain your reasoning.

$S - 2 = T$       $G = J + 13$       $P = I - 47.50$       $C + 273.15 = K$

$e = 6s$       $m = 8.96V$       $y = \frac{1}{12}x$       $t = \frac{d}{2.5}$

$g = 28.35z$

Table 1:

| independent variable | dependent variable |
|---|---|
| 20 | 8 |
| 58.85 | 23.54 |
| 804 | 321.6 |

Table 2:

| independent variable | dependent variable |
|---|---|
| 5 | 18 |
| 36 | 49 |
| 75 | 88 |

Table 3:

| independent variable | dependent variable |
|---|---|
| 2.5 | 22.4 |
| 20 | 179.2 |
| 75 | 672 |

Table 4:

| independent variable | dependent variable |
|---|---|
| 20 | $1\frac{2}{3}$ |
| 36 | 3 |
| 804 | 67 |

Table 5:

| independent variable | dependent variable |
|---|---|
| 58.85 | 11.35 |
| 175.5 | 128 |
| 804 | 756.5 |

Table 6:

| independent variable | dependent variable |
|---|---|
| 2.5 | 275.65 |
| 20 | 293.15 |
| 58.85 | 332 |

Table 7:

| independent variable | dependent variable |
| --- | --- |
| 5 | 3 |
| 20 | 18 |
| 36 | 34 |

Table 8:

| independent variable | dependent variable |
| --- | --- |
| 2.6 | 73.71 |
| 20 | 567 |
| 36 | 1,020.6 |

Table 9:

| independent variable | dependent variable |
| --- | --- |
| 2.6 | 15.6 |
| 36 | 216 |
| 58.85 | 353.1 |

## 19.2: Getting to Know an Equation

The equations in the previous activity represent situations.

- $S - 2 = T$ where $S$ is the number of sides on a polygon and $T$ is the number of triangles you can draw inside it (from one vertex to the others, without overlapping)

- $G = J + 13$ where $G$ is a day in the Gregorian calendar and $J$ is the same day in the Julian calendar

- $P = I - 47.50$ where $I$ is the amount of income and $P$ is the profit after \$47.50 in expenses

- $C + 273.15 = K$ where $C$ is a temperature in degrees Celsius and $K$ is the same temperature in Kelvin

- $e = 6s$ where $e$ is the total edge length of a regular tetrahedron and $s$ is the length of one side

- $m = 8.96V$ where $V$ is the volume of a piece of copper and $m$ is its mass

- $y = \frac{1}{12}x$ where $x$ is the number of eggs and $y$ is how many dozens that makes

- $t = \frac{d}{2.5}$ where $t$ is the amount of time it takes in seconds to jog a distance of $d$ meters at a constant speed of 2.5 meters per second

- $g = 28.35z$ where $g$ is the mass in grams and $z$ is the same amount in ounces

Your teacher will assign you one of these equations to examine more closely.

iM KH

1. Rewrite your equation using words. Use words like product, sum, difference, quotient, and term.

2. In the previous activity, you matched equations and tables. Copy the values from the table that matched your assigned equation into the first 3 rows of this table. Make sure to label what each column represents.

| independent variable: _____ | dependent variable: _____ |
|---|---|
|  |  |
|  |  |
|  |  |
| 60 |  |
|  | 300 |

3. Select one of the first 3 rows of the table and explain what those values mean in this situation.

4. Use your equation to find the values that complete the last 2 rows of the table. Explain your reasoning.

5. On graph paper, create a graph that represents this relationship. Make sure to label your axes.

## 19.3: Sharing Your Equation with Others

Create a visual display of your assigned relationships that includes:

- your equation along with an explanation of each variable
- a verbal description of the relationship
- your table
- your graph

If you have time, research more about your relationship and add more details or illustrations to help explain the situation.

# Learning Targets

### Lesson 1: Tape Diagrams and Equations

- I can tell whether or not an equation could represent a tape diagram.

- I can use a tape diagram to represent a situation.

### Lesson 2: Truth and Equations

- I can match equations to real life situations they could represent.

- I can replace a variable in an equation with a number that makes the equation true, and know that this number is called a solution to the equation.

### Lesson 3: Staying in Balance

- I can compare doing the same thing to the weights on each side of a balanced hanger to solving equations by subtracting the same amount from each side or dividing each side by the same number.

- I can explain what a balanced hanger and a true equation have in common.

- I can write equations that could represent the weights on a balanced hanger.

### Lesson 4: Practice Solving Equations and Representing Situations with Equations

- I can explain why different equations can describe the same situation.

- I can solve equations that have whole numbers, fractions, and decimals.

### Lesson 5: A New Way to Interpret $a$ over $b$

- I understand the meaning of a fraction made up of fractions or decimals, like $\frac{2.1}{0.07}$ or $\frac{\frac{4}{5}}{\frac{3}{2}}$.

- When I see an equation, I can make up a story that the equation might represent, explain what the variable represents in the story, and solve the equation.

iM KH

### Lesson 6: Write Expressions Where Letters Stand for Numbers

- I can use an expression that represents a situation to find an amount in a story.

- I can write an expression with a variable to represent a calculation where I do not know one of the numbers.

### Lesson 7: Revisit Percentages

- I can solve percent problems by writing and solving an equation.

### Lesson 8: Equal and Equivalent

- I can explain what it means for two expressions to be equivalent.

- I can use a tape diagram to figure out when two expressions are equal.

- I can use what I know about operations to decide whether two expressions are equivalent.

### Lesson 9: The Distributive Property, Part 1

- I can use a diagram of a rectangle split into two smaller rectangles to write different expressions representing its area.

- I can use the distributive property to help do computations in my head.

### Lesson 10: The Distributive Property, Part 2

- I can use a diagram of a split rectangle to write different expressions with variables representing its area.

### Lesson 11: The Distributive Property, Part 3

- I can use the distributive property to write equivalent expressions with variables.

### Lesson 12: Meaning of Exponents

- I can evaluate expressions with exponents and write expressions with exponents that are equal to a given number.

- I understand the meaning of an expression with an exponent like $3^5$.

### Lesson 13: Expressions with Exponents

- I can decide if expressions with exponents are equal by evaluating the expressions or by understanding what exponents mean.

### Lesson 14: Evaluating Expressions with Exponents

- I know how to evaluate expressions that have both an exponent and addition or subtraction.

- I know how to evaluate expressions that have both an exponent and multiplication or division.

### Lesson 15: Equivalent Exponential Expressions

- I can find solutions to equations with exponents in a list of numbers.

- I can replace a variable with a number in an expression with exponents and operations and use the correct order to evaluate the expression.

### Lesson 16: Two Related Quantities, Part 1

- I can create tables and graphs that show the relationship between two amounts in a given ratio.

- I can write an equation with variables that shows the relationship between two amounts in a given ratio.

### Lesson 17: Two Related Quantities, Part 2

- I can create tables and graphs to represent the relationship between distance and time for something moving at a constant speed.

- I can write an equation with variables to represent the relationship between distance and time for something moving at a constant speed.

### Lesson 18: More Relationships

- I can create tables and graphs that show different kinds of relationships between amounts.

- I can write equations that describe relationships with area and volume.

### Lesson 19: Tables, Equations, and Graphs, Oh My!

- I can create a table and a graph that represent the relationship in a given equation.

- I can explain what an equation tells us about the situation.

# Glossary

### area

Area is the number of square units that cover a two-dimensional region, without any gaps or overlaps.

For example, the area of region A is 8 square units. The area of the shaded region of B is $\frac{1}{2}$ square unit.

A      B

### base (of a parallelogram or triangle)

We can choose any side of a parallelogram or triangle to be the shape's base. Sometimes we use the word *base* to refer to the length of this side.

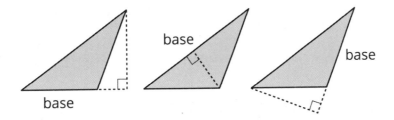

base     base     base

### base (of a prism or pyramid)

The word *base* can also refer to a face of a polyhedron.

A prism has two identical bases that are parallel. A pyramid has one base.

A prism or pyramid is named for the shape of its base.

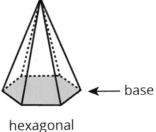

base →

base →

← base

pentagonal prism     hexagonal pyramid

### coefficient

A coefficient is a number that is multiplied by a variable.

For example, in the expression $3x + 5$, the coefficient of $x$ is 3. In the expression $y + 5$, the coefficient of $y$ is 1, because $y = 1 \cdot y$.

## compose

Compose means "put together." We use the word *compose* to describe putting more than one figure together to make a new shape.

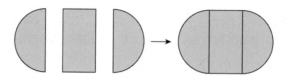

## coordinate plane

The coordinate plane is a system for telling where points are. For example. point $R$ is located at $(3, 2)$ on the coordinate plane, because it is three units to the right and two units up.

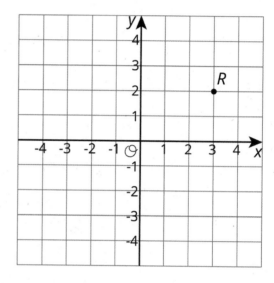

## cubed

We use the word *cubed* to mean "to the third power." This is because a cube with side length $s$ has a volume of $s \cdot s \cdot s$, or $s^3$.

## decompose

Decompose means "take apart." We use the word *decompose* to describe taking a figure apart to make more than one new shape.

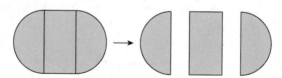

iM KH

## dependent variable

The dependent variable is the result of a calculation.

For example, a boat travels at a constant speed of 25 miles per hour. The equation $d = 25t$ describes the relationship between the boat's distance and time. The dependent variable is the distance traveled, because $d$ is the result of multiplying 25 by $t$.

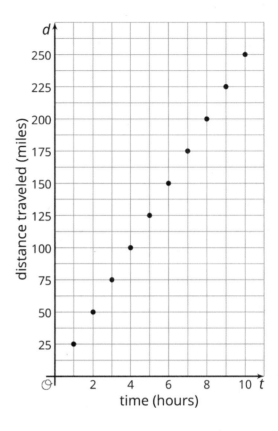

## double number line diagram

A double number line diagram uses a pair of parallel number lines to represent equivalent ratios. The locations of the tick marks match on both number lines. The tick marks labeled 0 line up, but the other numbers are usually different.

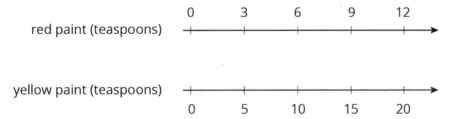

## edge

Each straight side of a polygon is called an edge.

For example, the edges of this polygon are segments $AB$, $BC$, $CD$, $DE$, and $EA$.

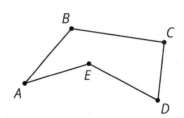

## equivalent expressions

Equivalent expressions are always equal to each other. If the expressions have variables, they are equal whenever the same value is used for the variable in each expression.

For example, $3x + 4x$ is equivalent to $5x + 2x$. No matter what value we use for $x$, these expressions are always equal. When $x$ is 3, both expressions equal 21. When $x$ is 10, both expressions equal 70.

## equivalent ratios

Two ratios are equivalent if you can multiply each of the numbers in the first ratio by the same factor to get the numbers in the second ratio. For example, $8 : 6$ is equivalent to $4 : 3$, because $8 \cdot \frac{1}{2} = 4$ and $6 \cdot \frac{1}{2} = 3$.

A recipe for lemonade says to use 8 cups of water and 6 lemons. If we use 4 cups of water and 3 lemons, it will make half as much lemonade. Both recipes taste the same, because  and  are equivalent ratios.

| cups of water | number of lemons |
|:---:|:---:|
| 8 | 6 |
| 4 | 3 |

## exponent

In expressions like $5^3$ and $8^2$, the 3 and the 2 are called exponents. They tell you how many factors to multiply. For example, $5^3 = 5 \cdot 5 \cdot 5$, and $8^2 = 8 \cdot 8$.

## face

Each flat side of a polyhedron is called a face. For example, a cube has 6 faces, and they are all squares.

## height (of a parallelogram or triangle)

The height is the shortest distance from the base of the shape to the opposite side (for a parallelogram) or opposite vertex (for a triangle).

We can show the height in more than one place, but it will always be perpendicular to the chosen base.

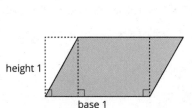

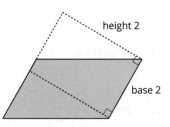

iM KH

## independent variable

The independent variable is used to calculate the value of another variable.

For example, a boat travels at a constant speed of 25 miles per hour. The equation $d = 25t$ describes the relationship between the boat's distance and time. The independent variable is time, because $t$ is multiplied by 25 to get $d$.

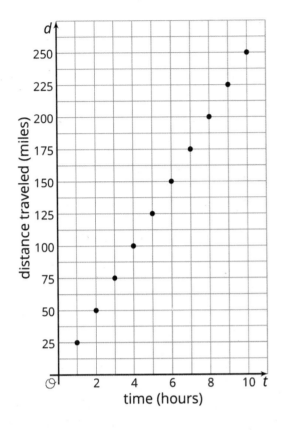

## long division

Long division is a way to show the steps for dividing numbers in decimal form. It finds the quotient one digit at a time, from left to right.

For example, here is the long division for $57 \div 4$.

$$
\begin{array}{r}
14.25 \\
4\overline{)57.00} \\
-4\phantom{7.00} \\
\hline
17\phantom{.00} \\
-16\phantom{.00} \\
\hline
10\phantom{0} \\
-8\phantom{0} \\
\hline
20 \\
-20 \\
\hline
0
\end{array}
$$

## meters per second

Meters per second is a unit for measuring speed. It tells how many meters an object goes in one second.

For example, a person walking 3 meters per second is going faster than another person walking 2 meters per second.

## net

A net is a two-dimensional figure that can be folded to make a polyhedron.

Here is a net for a cube.

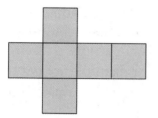

## opposite vertex

For each side of a triangle, there is one vertex that is not on that side. This is the opposite vertex.

For example, point $A$ is the opposite vertex to side $BC$.

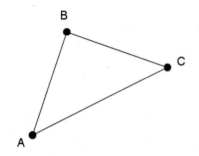

## pace

Pace is one way to describe how fast something is moving. Pace tells how much time it takes the object to travel a certain distance.

For example, Diego walks at a pace of 10 minutes per mile. Elena walks at a pace of 11 minutes per mile. Elena walks slower than Diego, because it takes her more time to travel the same distance.

## parallelogram

A parallelogram is a type of quadrilateral that has two pairs of parallel sides.

Here are two examples of parallelograms.

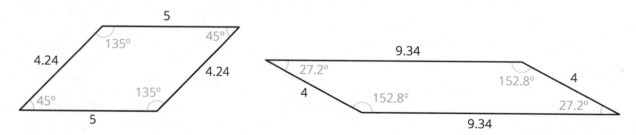

## per

The word *per* means "for each." For example, if the price is $5 per ticket, that means you will pay $5 *for each* ticket. Buying 4 tickets would cost $20, because $4 \cdot 5 = 20$.

## percent

The word *percent* means "for each 100." The symbol for percent is %.

For example, a quarter is worth 25 cents, and a dollar is worth 100 cents. We can say that a quarter is worth 25% of a dollar.

1 Quarter | 25¢

1 Dollar | 100¢

## percentage

A percentage is a rate per 100.

For example, a fish tank can hold 36 liters. Right now there is 27 liters of water in the tank. The percentage of the tank that is full is 75%.

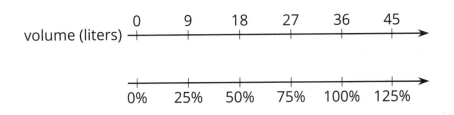

## polygon

A polygon is a closed, two-dimensional shape with straight sides that do not cross each other.

Figure $ABCDE$ is an example of a polygon.

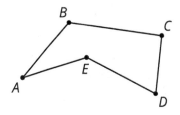

## polyhedron

A polyhedron is a closed, three-dimensional shape with flat sides. When we have more than one polyhedron, we call them polyhedra.

Here are some drawings of polyhedra.

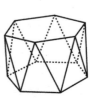

## prism

A prism is a type of polyhedron that has two bases that are identical copies of each other. The bases are connected by rectangles or parallelograms.

Here are some drawings of prisms.

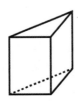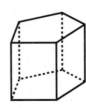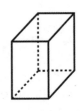

triangular prism     pentagonal prism     rectangular prism

## pyramid

A pyramid is a type of polyhedron that has one base. All the other faces are triangles, and they all meet at a single vertex.

Here are some drawings of pyramids.

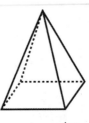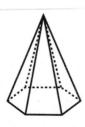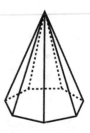

rectangular pyramid     hexagonal pyramid     heptagonal pyramid

## quadrilateral

A quadrilateral is a type of polygon that has 4 sides. A rectangle is an example of a quadrilateral. A pentagon is not a quadrilateral, because it has 5 sides.

## ratio

A ratio is an association between two or more quantities.

iM KH

For example, the ratio 3 : 2 could describe a recipe that uses 3 cups of flour for every 2 eggs, or a boat that moves 3 meters every 2 seconds. One way to represent the ratio 3 : 2 is with a diagram that has 3 blue squares for every 2 green squares.

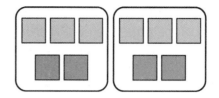

### reciprocal
Dividing 1 by a number gives the reciprocal of that number. For example, the reciprocal of 12 is $\frac{1}{12}$, and the reciprocal of $\frac{2}{5}$ is $\frac{5}{2}$.

### region
A region is the space inside of a shape. Some examples of two-dimensional regions are inside a circle or inside a polygon. Some examples of three-dimensional regions are the inside of a cube or the inside of a sphere.

### same rate
We use the words *same rate* to describe two situations that have equivalent ratios.

For example, a sink is filling with water at a rate of 2 gallons per minute. If a tub is also filling with water at a rate of 2 gallons per minute, then the sink and the tub are filling at the same rate.

### solution to an equation
A solution to an equation is a number that can be used in place of the variable to make the equation true.

For example, 7 is the solution to the equation $m + 1 = 8$, because it is true that $7 + 1 = 8$. The solution to $m + 1 = 8$ is not 9, because $9 + 1 \neq 8$.

### speed
Speed is one way to describe how fast something is moving. Speed tells how much distance the object travels in a certain amount of time.

For example, Tyler walks at a speed of 4 miles per hour. Priya walks at a speed of 5 miles per hour. Priya walks faster than Tyler, because she travels more distance in the same amount of time.

### squared
We use the word *squared* to mean "to the second power." This is because a square with side length $s$ has an area of $s \cdot s$, or $s^2$.

## surface area

The surface area of a polyhedron is the number of square units that covers all the faces of the polyhedron, without any gaps or overlaps.

For example, if the faces of a cube each have an area of 9 cm$^2$, then the surface area of the cube is $6 \cdot 9$, or 54 cm$^2$.

## table

A table organizes information into horizontal *rows* and vertical *columns*. The first row or column usually tells what the numbers represent.

For example, here is a table showing the tail lengths of three different pets. This table has four rows and two columns.

| pet | tail length (inches) |
|---|---|
| dog | 22 |
| cat | 12 |
| mouse | 2 |

## tape diagram

A tape diagram is a group of rectangles put together to represent a relationship between quantities.

For example, this tape diagram shows a ratio of 30 gallons of yellow paint to 50 gallons of blue paint.

| 10 | 10 | 10 |
|---|---|---|

| 10 | 10 | 10 | 10 | 10 |
|---|---|---|---|---|

If each rectangle were labeled 5, instead of 10, then the same picture could represent the equivalent ratio of 15 gallons of yellow paint to 25 gallons of blue paint.

## term

A term is a part of an expression. It can be a single number, a variable, or a number and a variable that are multiplied together. For example, the expression $5x + 18$ has two terms. The first term is $5x$ and the second term is 18.

## unit price

The unit price is the cost for one item or for one unit of measure. For example, if 10 feet of chain link fencing cost $150, then the unit price is $150 \div 10$, or $15 per foot.

## unit rate

A unit rate is a rate per 1.

iM KH

For example, 12 people share 2 pies equally. One unit rate is 6 people per pie, because $12 \div 2 = 6$. The other unit rate is $\frac{1}{6}$ of a pie per person, because $2 \div 12 = \frac{1}{6}$.

## variable

A variable is a letter that represents a number. You can choose different numbers for the value of the variable.

For example, in the expression $10 - x$, the variable is $x$. If the value of $x$ is 3, then $10 - x = 7$, because $10 - 3 = 7$. If the value of $x$ is 6, then $10 - x = 4$, because $10 - 6 = 4$.

## vertex

A vertex is a point where two or more edges meet. When we have more than one vertex, we call them vertices.

The vertices in this polygon are labeled $A$, $B$, $C$, $D$, and $E$.

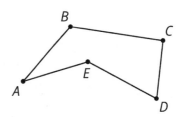

## volume

Volume is the number of cubic units that fill a three-dimensional region, without any gaps or overlaps.

For example, the volume of this rectangular prism is 60 units$^3$, because it is composed of 3 layers that are each 20 units$^3$.

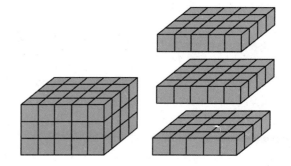

# Attributions

"Notice and Wonder" and "I Notice/I Wonder" are trademarks of the National Council of Teachers of Mathematics, reflecting approaches developed by the Math Forum (http://www.nctm.org/mathforum/), and used here with permission.

Images that are not the original work of Illustrative Mathematics are in the public domain or released under a Creative Commons Attribution (CC-BY) license, and include an appropriate citation. Images that are the original work of Illustrative Mathematics do not include such a citation.

## Image Attributions

Cardboard Boxes, by FrancisRomeo. Public Domain. Pixabay. https://pixabay.com/photos/pallet-goods-freighter-transport-1665471/.

Rain Guage, by Bidgee (Own Work). CC BY 3.0. Wikimedia Commons. https://commons.wikimedia.org/wiki/File:250mm_Rain_Gauge.jpg.

Aquarium récifal, by Serge Talfer (Self-photographed). Public Domain. Wikimedia Commons. https://commons.wikimedia.org/wiki/File:Aquarium_r%C3%A9cifal.JPG.

Salt-lick 4 Beentree, by Beentree (Own work). CC BY-SA 4.0. Wikimedia Commons. https://commons.wikimedia.org/wiki/File:Salt-lick_4_beentree.jpg.

By m01229. CC BY 2.0. Flickr. https://www.flickr.com/photos/39908901@N06/7925086692.

By skeeze. Public Domain. Pixabay. https://pixabay.com/en/giant-tortoise-tortoise-reptile-zoo-597624/.

August 3rd London Olympics 2012 stadium hurdles, by Steve Flair. CC BY 2.0. Wikimedia Commons. https://commons.wikimedia.org/wiki/File:August_3rd_London_Olympics_2012_stadium_hurdles.jpg.

# Notes

# Notes